An Introduction to The Lightning Process®

The Complete Strategy For Success

Phil Parker
Do Dip E Hyp Psyc CMPNLP

NIPTON PUBLISHING
River Plate House, 7-11 Finsbury Circus, London EC2M 7DH

First published in 2007 by Nipton Publishing
Revised in 2009
Revised in 2010

A CIP catalogue record for this book is available from the British Library.

ISBN 9780955648205

Every effort has been made to obtain the necessary permissions with reference to copyright material, both illustrative and quoted. We apologise for any omissions in this respect and will be pleased to make appropriate acknowledgements in any future editions. Please note that some client's names have been changed by their request to protect their identity.

Printed in the UK
Cover design by Mulberry Advertising

I'd like to thank so many inspirational people for their help and assistance whilst writing this book.

Special thanks go to my amazing family, my hard working Head Office team and the inspirational members of the Register of Lightning Process Practitioners who have dedicated their lives to making others' lives better.

A heartfelt thank you must also go to the pioneers of NLP, Hypnotherapy and Osteopathy who have inspired me so much, especially Dr Still, Milton Erickson, Richard Bandler and John Grinder, Connirae and Steve Andreas and Robert Dilts. Thanks also to Dr Eric Dolgin for Dr Still's quote on page 40.

Final thanks go to all those I had the privilege to work with whilst developing the Lightning Process. Who have inspired me with their personal bravery and determination to get their lives back and who, through their endeavours, showed others what was possible.

Contents

Introduction

The Purpose of this Book

There's been a huge amount of interest in the Lightning Process (LP) over the last decade and this book has been written to meet the demand for more information on this intriguing and important approach to creating change. It's designed as an interactive guide to:

- Help you make an informed decision as to whether this is the right approach for you at this stage in your life.
- To prepare you as much as possible to get full benefit from taking the Lightning Process seminars.

The fact that you've bought this book and started reading it means you have a keen interest in discovering how lives can be changed for the better, and have taken the first step, *action*.

You will probably be thinking one of the following things about making the changes you desire in your life, or if you are reading this to help someone else, in their life; you might think that to achieve those goals will be either:

- Extremely difficult
- Quite hard
- Complicated
- Easy
- Effortless

But interestingly, however you are currently thinking about the ease or difficulty of that change, there are just two things you need to know:

1. Because you've opened the book and started to read it, you must believe it's somehow possible to make the changes you desire or you wouldn't have even bothered getting this far.

2. The Lightning Process and this book, can teach you how to change regardless of how easy or difficult that change is going to be.

So, allow yourself to recognise where you are in terms of your hopefulness as we continue what could be the most important journey of your life.

That journey is best started by discovering the stories of some of the people who know the Process best - those who've travelled the road that lies ahead of you and have made fundamental, positive changes in their lives by using the Process and why I embarked on my journey to designing it. One family's extraordinary story is summed up in these few lines that Anne wrote about her son:

> *Thank you for having come up with the Process as having our son back to health has been the best Christmas present possible. You trained my son Joseph in the Lightning Process last week. He is eighteen today and life has not been so good for him in a long time. Thank you seems too tame. You have given him back his life.*
>
> *Today he has spent the day recording a demo at a studio with his band, then he watched his team (Arsenal) lose to Newcastle (oops!), now he is out with his girlfriend. Since our return he has been up to Reading on a train on his own to visit a friend, he has been out shopping, to the pub etc. This time last week he was pretty much housebound - now he is up and at 'em!*
>
> *I have met with cynicism and disbelief about the Process but I don't really mind, it has worked for Joseph and that's more important than anyone's ill informed opinion. I think that I am having more trouble readjusting than he is - I am going through a mix of happiness for him, then I am overwhelmed by it all and quite tearful. It has been a long time of anxiety. I am so*

> *glad we heard about you and decided to take a chance; it paid off better than I could ever have imagined.*

Whilst that story unfolds, we can turn our focus to Charlie. Charlie hated only one thing in her life, and she hated it with a passion. It influenced her every thought, action and dream. It was a constant yardstick that she measured everything by, her passionate hatred created a constant commentary, the soundtrack of her life.

Charlie hated only one thing in her life. Herself.

On the other side of town, Ray was an extremely successful businessman. Everything in *his* life had worked out wonderfully; great house in *the* location, beautiful and intelligent partner, gorgeous kids, smart car and big pension. So why did he feel so dreadful everyday, why did his heart beat uncontrollably when he was just resting, why did his legs just refuse to work one morning, why did everything that he thought was important, seem to give him no joy?

I had studied with some of the best personal development trainers in the world, read the most cutting edge books, and had eventually become a fairly well thought of figure in the world of change, and yet there were still some clients, like Charlie and Ray, who I felt I should be able to help because of my skills, track record and depth of experience, but for whom nothing seemed to work. This didn't surprise Charlie, dozens of other professionals had tried and failed - she had become resigned to being a hopeless case.

Now, no one would claim to be able to sort out everyone who consulted them, but these people really needed and desperately wanted help. In addition, they often had some of the most common and horrifically debilitating problems, such as:

- Low self-esteem, self doubt and even self hatred
- Fear of failure
- Guilt

- Anxiety
- Stress and struggle
- Depression
- Feeling overwhelmed
- Myalgic Encephalomyopathy/Chronic Fatigue Syndrome (CFS/ME)
- Obsessive Compulsive Disorder (OCD)

Whilst many of my clients with these issues responded really well, others, like Charlie and Ray, struggled to achieve any change. I kept wondering, “What was the difference?”

From the extraordinary successes I'd had whilst working with others I knew the tools I was using were really powerful, but they just weren't making any real difference in these cases. I felt there had to be a way of helping them.

Months of research set me on a course which was to revolutionise my work, change the lives of thousands for the better and lead to you reading this book. The result of this important research was the development of the Lightning Process.

But just before we begin to explore the Lightning Process, I'd like to say thanks to Charlie, Ray and all the others for stimulating the creation of this path to freedom. Without them helping me to discover what was keeping them stuck and how to change it, it wouldn't have been possible for all those who have followed them.

And, if you met Charlie or Ray now, you simply wouldn't recognise them from the description at the beginning of this chapter because both of them now live lives that they love.

Applications and Related Programmes

The Lightning Process has become something of a hot issue in the press and media over recent years particularly because of the extraordinary success it's had in dealing with a number of different conditions. As a result, a number of you reading this book will probably be interested in the Lightning Process from the perspective of finding out how you can get similar changes.

There will also be many other readers who don't have one of the profoundly debilitating conditions that the Lightning Process has successfully helped. The book has been written as much for you as it has for them because although the Lightning Process has been used extensively in those fields, resolving 'stuckness' is just one application of this incredible tool. As you will discover in these pages it's been applied to any areas of life where people would like to become more successful, happier and more fulfilled.

In recent years I have also developed specialist programmes using some of the technology of the LP, such as our Phil Parker Peak Performance (P4) and Powerzone programmes for application in business and education, to help people get similar levels of success in those areas.

As you read through the book you will find some chapters that may refer to issues that aren't ones you suffer from. However I'd still recommend you read these chapters as they are a powerful demonstration of how even the most debilitated and apparently hopeless cases can be resolved simply and rapidly. For those of you who might decide to skip chapters I've included a standard ending to many of the chapters about what to do next, so please excuse the repetition for those of you who read each chapter as suggested.

The question I would ask you to hold in your mind as you read the book is "If these people have resolved their difficulties, then what might be possible for me?"

Throughout the book there are exercises for you to do. These are designed to help you make changes at some level and I would strongly recommend that you keep a pen and paper handy so that you can work through them as you go along.

Chapter 1
The Beginning

The Lightning Process: What is it?

The briefest definition I can give of the Lightning Process is that it's a simple, elegant and powerful process that is designed to teach you how to get a life you love. It is a complete strategy for success.

On one level this sums it up very well, and yet this description leaves more questions than it answers. This is the problem with brief, one line descriptions of complex events, as Einstein said:

> *Our job is to make things as simple as possible, but no simpler.*

and this very much applies to the Lightning Process. The brief opening definition, although good, doesn't tell us too much about what the Process actually is.

Fortunately we can also describe the basic elements of the Process:

The Lightning Process three day seminar is an interactive journey of discovery that takes approximately 12 hours to unfold and is designed to teach people:

1. About the Physical Emergency Response (PER) which the body creates in response to any threats - we will be covering this in more detail later, and what happens if it is constantly switched on.
2. How to **Spot** when the PER is occurring.
3. How to **Calm** the PER through specific steps using movement, posture, and coaching. These steps are not vigorous or physically demanding and can be tailored to meet the capabilities of even the most debilitated clients.
4. How to make this change to their physiology permanent by practising the steps so that they become automatic, leading to health and well-being.

Although this description is useful it can't really stand in for the material covered in 12 hours of training.

As the Designer of the Lightning Process, I obviously have more experience of the Process than anyone else but it's still quite surprising to find how difficult it is to create an adequate definition or description that's detailed enough and yet doesn't go on for pages and pages.

The Process itself is simple, elegant and powerful. However the structure that lies beneath this process and creates the change, its specific design, individual elements and the teaching of the Process itself, are extremely complex and sophisticated. This should come as no surprise when you consider that more than a decade of research, experimentation and exploration has gone into creating it. It has been reassessed, stripped down and refined many times over that period.

Although the definitions and descriptions I've provided are quite brief, I've found they are the best ones to use and there is a very important reason for this, which is in fact one of the first steps in the Lightning Process.

The Power of Simplicity and the Dangers of Prediction

I've used these brief definitions and descriptions because although they are incomplete, they are the best way for you to begin to get a sense of what's possible for you from using the Process, even if you've been stuck somewhere in your life for a long time.

We need to begin with some understanding of how our brain works. Our brain processes information by looking for patterns and familiarity, as this is a valuable skill for learning and survival. This ability allows us to predict things based on a combination of:

- The first, tiniest fragment of information about what's just starting to happen around us, and

- Our past experience.

To illustrate this, I'd like you to imagine we live in a village surrounded by a wood. We know from past experience that dangerous beasts live in the wood. When we think about going into the wood, we will take a spear (or someone who can run less fast than us!) to prepare us for the possibility of meeting the dangerous beasts.

Unfortunately, this brain function can also hold us back, as it can equally create un-useful expectations about new things. If we know that dangerous beasts have been found in the woods we might continue to avoid the woods long after the beasts have left. We could possibly avoid all woods, even those full of plants laden with easily harvestable foods, because we fear that they might be filled with similarly dangerous beasts.

In this case, the incorrect assumption that new things (*the new woods*) are similar to old things (*the old woods*) which we've experienced before, forces us to treat them as the same kind of thing and we put the new things (*the new woods*) into a category (*dangerous*) that they don't necessarily fit into.

For those of you familiar with spell checkers or predictive text on mobile phones, you will know how those electronic brains try and predict what word you are looking to use based on the first few letters and which words are most commonly used by you. Sometimes this is really helpful at making our documents accurate and our typing faster but sometimes when it predicts incorrectly, it makes our documents inaccurate, our typing slower and can be very irritating.

In the past, when I provided people with a detailed description of the Lightning Process, I found that they immediately began to categorise the Process based on what they already knew, putting it into a pigeonhole of something they could categorise.

This is reasonable but of course problematic. For example, if someone is personally trying to resolve a long-term problem (such as depression) and already knows about a set of solutions such as life coaching or Neuro-linguistic Programming (NLP) then it means these solutions either haven't worked for them or in their mind are inappropriate to use with those stuck issues.

If they put the Lightning Process in the same pigeonhole as the unsuccessful approach by thinking "*The Lightning Process sounds like life coaching to me*" they will dismiss it out of hand, because they think it's the same kind of thing. Obviously this kind of thinking is reasonable but not always helpful.

The Lightning Process was designed with some reference to a number of different approaches, these include NLP, life coaching and osteopathy - but this is not an exhaustive list. It's vital to notice that although you might be able to see some slight similarities between the Lightning Process and some other approaches, it should be viewed as something different, something that doesn't quite fit with what you already know.

One of the core ways it displays its fundamental difference to other approaches is that it gets such different results from them.

Many people who take a training seminar in the Lightning Process have often previously visited excellent practitioners of NLP, life coaching and osteopathy etc., but the combination of these approaches hasn't helped them to make the changes they wished for. However when they apply the Lightning Process they then find they can get those changes that had previously eluded them. I recommend that you keep this idea in your mind throughout your exploration of the Process.

What you'll get from reading this book

This book is an introduction to the Lightning Process. It has been primarily designed to get you thinking about what's possible in those areas where nothing seems to change. To help you stretch your mind and explore what kind of future you'd like to have so that you can decide if you'd like to reap the same kinds of rewards others have by using the Lightning Process.

It is not a 'how to do the Lightning Process' book, although it was originally intended to be published as such. Many people asked me to write a self-help guide to teach the reader how to apply the Lightning Process to their life. It seemed an important and valuable book to write, but it soon became clear that there was one issue that a book format couldn't overcome which was, how could you, the reader, recognise your own blind spots without expert help.

Whichever way I tried to present the LP, so that I could ensure consistently good levels of results comparable to visiting a practitioner, I couldn't find a workable way around this key sticking point.

As a result, I decided that this book would not be a 'how to do the Lightning Process' for two important reasons:

1. Due to complexities of some of our readers' issues and often combined with a history littered with promises of 'cures' that were never delivered, I didn't want to produce yet another book that promised the world but, because of the limits of the format, delivered very little.
2. For your safety and future it is important to avoid using the Process without correct training. Doing this would create very variable results, with some readers making huge changes and others just feeling more stuck. But even more importantly, the people who remained stuck would naturally think they'd used the Process properly and it just didn't work for them, rather than realising they'd just not been implementing it effectively. It's so vital to avoid this scenario, as it would ruin the opportunity for those people to make huge changes using the Process under supervised conditions by trying to make a half understood version work.

Instead, this book is designed to begin to stimulate those parts of your brain that know all about change and like rolling a snowball down a steep snow covered hillside, just a small initial movement can produce a huge result.

EXERCISE:

Write down, in the space below details of a time when you have experienced spontaneous change in your life; where watching a film, reading a book, learning something or being around someone leads you to see things differently.

Chapter 2
Stretching Your Mind: Part One

How does it work?

The Lightning Process is a journey of exploration to discover what is responsible for the continuing issues and problems in your life and then finding how you can free yourself from those issues. There are some core components of the Process that are essential for creating the change you desire. These are listed below and are what I have called exploratory '*how*' statements. Each statement is related to one of the core concepts (CC) of the Lightning Process, which is in brackets at the end of each statement.

EXERCISE:

Start by looking through the following '*how*' statements; you don't need to write your answers at this point as you will have another opportunity to do so later. Begin to consider whether you:

Currently subscribe to these concepts and ideas - and if you don't, what might be possible if you did?

The Lightning Process will help you discover:

- *How* much more influential you are in your life and health than you might ever imagine (CC: you are extremely influential in your life and health).
- *How* so many of the reasons why you are not having the great life and health you wish for are due to physical and psychological patterns (CC: these patterns exert a huge influence on your health and life).
- *How* often you will not even notice these destructive patterns as they are just not within your conscious awareness or control? *How* you are not to blame for them and *how* it is very difficult to identify them without expert help or training (CC: these patterns often run without any conscious input from us).

- *How* much the body influences the brain and the brain influences the body (CC: our brains and bodies can influence each other).
- *How* to develop a whole new set of effective tools that will allow you to live the life you love (CC: we can learn to influence those physical and physiological patterns).

If, as you look through these ideas, you find it hard to agree with one or two of them then stop and consider what would be the benefit of *acting* as if they were correct assumptions. We find that until you have begun to embrace these ideas using the Lightning Process, creating change will be very hard work, and who would want such important work to be hard? We will explore these core concepts more fully in the next few pages.

Training or Treatment?

Some people think that the Lightning Process should work regardless of whether you agree with some of its core concepts or not; this however comes from a misunderstanding as to what the Lightning Process is.

EXERCISE:

Please write down the answers to these questions:

1. Is the Lightning Process a training programme or a treatment/therapy?
2. What are the differences between those two things? (The next two questions might help.)

   a) When a doctor gives you a pill do YOU have to do anything other than take it to get the benefits from it?
   b) When you attend a training course do YOU have to do anything other than turn up to get results from the training?

In a treatment or therapy, the therapist has a very active role in providing an effective remedy for the patient. The patient therefore, has a much more passive role as often all they need to do is attend the appointment and the work will be done to them. It would be surprising to visit an acupuncturist and have to put your own needles in or visit a dentist and put fillings in your own teeth.

It's also worth looking at where the word *patient* comes from. It's derived from the Latin word *patiens*, meaning 'one who endures' or 'one who suffers'. Similarly the adjective *patience* means 'enduring trying circumstances with even temper'. It is also the root of the word *passive*.

Some authorities have argued recently that the term should be dropped because it underlines the inferior status of recipients of health care (Neuberger, J. (1999). 'Let's do away with patients.' (*British Medical Journal* 318: 1756-8). For them, 'the active patient is a contradiction in terms and it is the assumption underlying the passivity that is the most dangerous'.

Unfortunately, the other main word used in medicine and treatments instead of patient is *client*, whose Latin root *cliens* means 'One who is obliged to make supplications to a powerful figure for material assistance'. This obviously carries a sense of subservience!

In a training programme the roles are quite different, as here the participant will not get much benefit from just turning up, instead they have to actively participate in the learning process. The more they work, following their trainerv's instructions, and the more receptive they are to the guidance and feedback of their tutor, the better they will learn.

The origin of the word *train* also comes from a Latin word (*traginare*) which means to draw out. Later this led to its use as the trailing/following part of a skirt or the 'train' of a wedding dress and also in the railway industry as 'a train of carriages'. So training literally means to 'follow the teachings'.

From the exploration of the differences between training and treatment it becomes clear that the Lightning Process is very much a training process. As with any training process the success is dependent on the effective delivery and knowledge of the trainer but even more vitally it depends on the attitude and application of the participant. It's not that relevant how clever the participant is but how open they are to learning and implementing new information, and how they deal with feedback when they go off track. Many studies show that the beliefs a participant has about the training (for example how interesting, important, easy, etc. it is going to be), the beliefs they have about themselves as learners and their beliefs about how successful they are going to be are all key factors in influencing their success.

EXERCISE:

Imagine if you were a French teacher and you had only one space left on your course and two students wish to join.

The first student says:

> *I hate learning, I find learning languages almost impossible, I have no interest in French but my bosses say I must learn it. I'm sure it will be really difficult and I'm not certain I can be bothered to put the hours in if it gets hard. I suspect I'm just one of those people who can't learn French anyway.*

The second says:

> *I love learning, I've already successfully mastered five languages and I'm really interested in French and can imagine how great it will be to speak it fluently. I'm sure there will be some challenges on the way, but I know it will be easy and there's no obstacle that I can't get round if I put my mind to it. After all, if others can do it, it can't be that hard.*

Which one is almost certainly going to be a more successful, committed student and a faster learner?

Exploring the Core Concepts

The core concepts are:

Concept 1. You are extremely influential in your life and health.

Concept 2. Your physical and psychological patterns exert a huge influence on your health and life.

Concept 3. Your patterns are often unconscious.

Concept 4. Your brain and body can influence each other.

Concept 5. You can learn to influence these patterns.

EXERCISE:
Do I agree with each of the core concepts?

Concept 1. You are extremely influential in your life and health. YES/NO

Concept 2. Your physical and psychological patterns exert a huge influence on your health and life. YES/NO

Concept 3. Your patterns are often unconscious. YES/NO

Concept 4. Your brain and body can influence each other. YES/NO

Concept 5. You can learn to influence these patterns. YES/NO

If you wish to benefit from the Lightning Process, my experience indicates that you need to begin by considering what evidence you have that might support your agreement with those core concepts listed above. We've found that the Process can help people who have yet to decide whether they agree with these concepts or not, but it definitely takes much longer to effectively train them to use the Lightning Process if they don't. They are also, unsurprisingly, much more likely to be in the small percentage of people who get very little results from the training seminars.

So to help yourself, we recommend you begin to steer your thinking in a more valuable direction by answering the question below while you consider each concept.

EXERCISE:
What evidence do I have that helps me agree with the core concepts?

Concept 1 and 2:
You are extremely influential in your life and health; and your physical and psychological patterns can affect your life and health.

Brain and Body

Medical science has known for a long time that we have a great influence on our health and body. It's noticed that our beliefs about the likely effectiveness of a treatment affects how we respond to that treatment. This is the reason that every new drug has to be 'double blind' tested before its effects can be documented. A 'double blind' is where the people being tested for a response to the drug are divided into two groups. One group is given a pill which has the drug in it, while the other group is given an identical looking pill but this one has none of the drug in it (a placebo). Neither the individuals in the groups or the person distributing the drugs know which drugs are real and which are placebos.

The two groups are then observed to see what the effects are of taking the actual drug compared to the so called 'placebo effect' which are the effects produced by just thinking you are taking a drug.

This produces interesting results. What follows are just a few examples taken from the vast wealth of research into how much our expectations powerfully influence our response to treatment. It's worth noting that if there wasn't any influence of our brain over our body then there would be no real need to test every drug in this way.

Some of the cases that follow come from an important article on the subject by Margaret Talbot in which she considers the evidence from many different journals and sources. If you'd like to read the article in full, it can be found on the New York Times magazine website ('The Placebo Prescription' by Margaret Talbot, *New York Times Magazine*, January 9, 2000).

The Research into Placebos: Prozac and Placebo

Irving Kirsch, a psychologist at the University of Connecticut, has studied the effectiveness of Prozac and similar drugs compared to placebos. His findings suggest that much of the results from taking these drugs may be almost entirely due to the placebo effect. He and his colleague, Guy Saperstein, analysed nineteen clinical trials of antidepressants. They concluded that the expectation of improvement, not adjustments in brain chemistry, accounted for 75 percent of the drugs' effectiveness (Kirsch 1998). "The critical factor", says Kirsch, "Is our beliefs about what's going to happen to us. You don't have to rely on drugs to see profound transformation."

A prior study by Saperstein analysed thirty-nine other studies which had been carried out between 1974 and 1995. These were of depressed patients who had been treated with drugs, psychotherapy or a combination of both. He found that 50 percent of the drug effect was due to the placebo response.

Painkilling Placebos

Studies by Professor Jon-Kar Zubieta from the University of Michigan, using a brain-scanning technique (Positron Emission Tomography), showed that the expectation a patient had of getting some pain relief by taking a drug activated the brain's own painkilling mechanisms.

The Michigan team looked at mu-opioid receptors, a class of receptors involved in endogenous pain relief. The activity of these receptors was higher when a 'painkilling' placebo was given with a painful stimulus, suggesting that the placebo stimulated the release of endogenous painkilling chemicals in the brain. (Zubieta JK et al. 'Placebo effects mediated by endogenous opioid activity on mu-opioid receptors'. *Journal of Neuroscience 2005*; 25(34): 7754–62)

Other Studies

The interesting findings from the countless studies in this field include the following. Doctors discovered that they could successfully eliminate warts by simply painting them with a brightly coloured, inert (i.e. had no therapeutic ingredients) dye and promising the patients that the warts would be gone when the colour wore off.

Researchers studying asthmatics found that they could produce dilation (opening) of the airways by just telling people they were inhaling a bronchodilator, even when they weren't.

Patients gained as much pain relief following a wisdom-tooth extraction with the application of fake ultrasound (i.e. a machine that had been altered so that it wouldn't produce any of the therapeutic ultrasound signal, however, it appeared to be working because all of its lights and indicators were on) as from a real one. This worked as long as the patient and, importantly, the therapist thought that the machine was on.

In a study of eleven different trials, 52 percent of colitis (inflammation of the bowel) patients treated with placebo reported feeling better and, amazingly, 50 percent of the inflamed intestines actually looked better when assessed with a sigmoid scope.

Sham Operations

In the wild years of the 1960s, Leonard Cobb, a cardiologist, conducted a trial in which he compared two approaches to angina. The first was the standard surgical approach for angina which involved doctors making small incisions in the chest and tying knots in some heart arteries to try to increase blood flow to the heart (it had a promising track record of producing positive results in 90 percent of patients). The second approach was one in which Cobb made the incisions but did not tie off the arteries, 'placebo surgery.' The sham operations proved to be just as successful. The procedure, known as internal mammary ligation, was soon abandoned.

Allergies and Placebos

In another experiment, asthmatic patients breathed in a vapour that researchers had told them was a chemical irritant or allergen, which would therefore be expected to produce breathing difficulties for them. Nearly 50 percent of the patients experienced the expected breathing problems, with some developing full-blown attacks. They were then 'treated' with a substance that the researchers told them was a bronchodilating (airway opening) medicine, and they recovered immediately. In fact, both the 'irritant' and the 'medicine' were nothing more than a vapour made from a weak saltwater solution.

Researchers in Japan tested fifty-seven high school boys for their sensitivity to allergens. The boys completed questionnaires regarding past experiences with plants, including lacquer trees (which can cause itchy rashes in a similar way to poison oak and poison ivy).

The boys who reported having severe reactions to the poisonous trees were then blindfolded. Researchers brushed one of their arms with leaves from a lacquer tree but told the boys that they were chestnut tree leaves (a tree that doesn't cause rashes). Their other arm was then brushed with chestnut tree leaves whilst the researchers told them the leaves had came from a lacquer tree.

Within minutes of the brushing, an intriguing set of findings were reported. The arm that the boys believed had been brushed with the poisonous tree began to react, as though it had been in contact with the lacquer tree. It turned red and began to develop a bumpy, itchy rash. However, in most cases, the arm that had contact with the real poison did not react. (Gardiner Morse, 'The nocebo effect,' *Hippocrates*, November 1999, Hippocrates.com).

The Value of Placebos

The placebo effect is often considered by science to be an annoyance but actually it's one of the most magical things our body does. When people respond to non-drugs as if they were powerful drugs, what is happening is they are activating their natural healing ability. Equally, when people don't think something will work, that belief will have a negative effect on their response to treatment, or in this case, training.

EXERCISE for concept 1:
When have I experienced for myself, or seen someone else influence their health in a positive or negative way?

EXERCISE for concept 2:
It's clear that physical patterns can affect health; but when have I experienced for myself, or seen someone else influence their life in a positive or negative way, just by what they thought?

Concept 3 and 4:
Your patterns are often unconscious and your brain and body can influence each other.

When looking at a series of drugs trials for three different types of anti-migraine medicine researchers found some intriguing results (Pain Vol 146 Issue 3 Pages 261-269, 5 December 2009 M.Amanzioab, et al). They noticed that many of the people taking the placebos instead of the real drugs experienced side effects from taking the pills, which contained no active medicines whatsoever. This suggests that the people's anticipation of the side effects was actively creating changes in their body's physiology.

Even more interestingly, the side effects they had corresponded to the expected side effects of each particular type of drug; so 'for example, anorexia and memory difficulties, which are typical adverse events of anticonvulsants, were present only in the placebo arm of these trials'.

Similarly, Bernie Siegel M.D reports a very interesting example, from drug research trials, of the mind body influence in his thought provoking book *Love, Medicine and Miracles*, "In chemotherapy trials, some patients receiving placebo treatment, lost their hair if they were told that it was a side effect of the product they were taking." (Siegel, B.S. (1986) *Love, Medicine & Miracles: Lessons Learned About Self-Healing from a Surgeon's Experience with Exceptional Patients.* New York: Harper Perennial. P133)

So some of the group who took a pill (full of nothing but chalk and sugar) believing it to be chemotherapy, lost their hair. That is quite impressive to see such a powerful physical response to nothing but a *belief*.

If I were to ask you to think very hard and try and make your eyelashes fall out, it would be unlikely that you would succeed. The reason that those people got that powerful response was because they weren't consciously trying to make their hair fall out, they just *unconsciously* knew it would.

EXERCISE for concept 3:
When have I experienced for myself, or seen someone else automatically approaching or doing something (which is either valuable or destructive) in a habitual or very practised way without apparently even thinking about it?

EXERCISE for concept 4:
When have I experienced for myself, or seen someone else influence their mind in a positive or negative way, just by what they physically did? And were they able to influence their body by what they were thinking?

EXERCISE for concept 5:
When have I experienced for myself, or seen someone else change something that was a good or bad habit, or physical response or a way of thinking? Physical response examples

can include things such as starting an exercise plan and after a few weeks finding you could run much further than before.

Chapter 3
Applications

Who might benefit from the Lightning Process?

Although it was developed as a result of working with people who had had quite complex problems for some time, I've found that it's such a powerful process that it also produces amazingly rapid change with most of the common issues that can prevent our lives from being great.

Common Problems

Below are just some of the common problems people have told us they have resolved using the Process:

- Addictions: drugs, alcohol etc.
- Anger
- Anxiety, panic attacks and fear
- Compulsive behaviours
- Depression
- Eating disorders
- Fear of failure
- Guilt and shame
- Inability to communicate
- Insomnia
- Low self-esteem, self doubt and even self hatred
- Motivation
- Obsessive Compulsive Disorder (OCD)
- Feeling overwhelmed
- Perfectionism
- Poor time keeping
- Procrastination and 'laziness'
- Prolonged grief
- Repetitive and obsessive thoughts
- Shyness
- Smoking
- Stage fright
- Stress and struggle
- Weight issues and dieting

Physical Conditions

People have reported that it has also produced amazingly rapid change with a whole range of physical conditions that they had suffered from. Some examples include:

- Back and neck problems
- CFS/ME
- Chemical sensitivity
- Chronic pain
- Eczema
- Electro-magnetic sensitivity
- Food and chemical sensitivity
- Fibromyalgia (FM)
- Headaches/ Migraines
- Multiple Sclerosis (MS)
- Muscle fatigue
- Psoriasis

Enhancing Success

The LP and related programmes, which I have subsequently developed from the LP, are brilliantly effective for enhancing the following:

- Confidence
- Discovering what you really want
- Happiness
- Interview performance
- Relationships
- Sleep

As you can see from these lists, it seems that anywhere where you are not achieving your best, whether the results you are getting in you life are disastrous, average or quite good already, you can use the LP for working out how to stop those destructive patterns and enhance your current skills and abilities.

Chapter 4
Stretching Your Mind: Part Two

How successful is it?

This is an extremely important question in that you will obviously want to know what kind of results have been achieved using the Process. In answering this it highlights one of the key elements of the Process - identifying that the single most powerful ingredient to success is you.

We will cover our success rates later but to make better sense of the question it's important to first consider the idea that you are the most powerful ingredient in the success of the Process. This naturally follows on from the section that discusses whether the Process is a training programme or a treatment.

Before anyone is accepted onto the training seminar their practitioner will spend some time working with them to make sure they are adequately prepared for the training - we will cover this in more depth later on.

One of the most important points of these discussions is for the participant to understand that they will need to apply the tools of the training both during and after the seminars.

I have found that it's essential for participants to recognise that by just turning up for the training programme they will not get the same results as previous graduates and that they will need to be instrumental in making the training programme useful, by applying it appropriately.

Only one person has the power, and therefore the most influence to do this: *you*. This defines you as the most important player in the LP seminar, and therefore in your future. Having said that, you are not alone in journey. Knowing that all great athletes, top performers and explorers need a great back up team your practitioner does not expect you to go it alone. They will be there for you before, during and after the course to help you keep putting the training into practice in anyway they can, for as long as you need.

Measuring Results

From this understanding it is clear that the success an individual gains as a result of attending the training is dependent on:

1. **The quality of the materials of the training**
   This includes the concepts, theories, tools and techniques that are the components of the training programme.

2. **The quality of delivery of the training and support provided by the practitioner**
   This includes their ability to deliver the training in an understandable and effective way. They will also need to have an appropriate depth of knowledge about the subject to be able to tailor their delivery of the seminar's contents and support/coach the individuals in an effective manner.

3. **The degree of application of the participant**
   This includes a commitment to ensure they understand the concepts, theories, tools and techniques that are the components of the training programme. To be willing to ask appropriate questions to enhance their understanding, be ready to carry out the tasks and exercises suggested by the practitioner and training and be open to feedback at all times about their performance. To also have a belief that it is possible that they can attain the results the seminar suggests is possible and that they are capable of doing that.

In the Lightning Process, the first two of the previous points above are demonstrated by its track record of effectiveness. All of the Lightning Process Practitioners have experience of successfully delivering the material to and supporting large numbers of people who have been able to get life changing benefits from the Process.

The Process is continuously developed in line with best practice and the latest research. The practitioners are trained to be consistent in the quality of their delivery, they have to attend professional development courses and are supervised on an ongoing basis.

The element therefore, that is most unpredictable is the third point - the participant. This is why we stress the importance of the participant's contribution to the training process as it's the main variable that will dictate the effectiveness of the Process.

In spite of this unpredictable factor, there is only a small variation in results. This is a reflection both on the effectiveness of the training programme, the practitioners, the pre-training preparation and coaching process and especially the level to which participants apply the training effectively.

To date we have found that the vast majority of people get the results that they wish for by attending the training. For example in a recent survey 81.3% of 1092 people with CFS/ME, and 80% of 440 people with Depression reported that they felt they had recovered after the LP seminar. Those are quite staggering results when you consider that these are both good examples of issues that many people struggle to resolve in the long-term.

The few percent of people who don't get the results they wish for have so far been those who haven't felt able to put the training into practice as fully as they hoped they would. In our recent snapshot survey of 1297 following day three of the training people only two felt that the training wasn't appropriate for their needs.

Influence

Influence is a term that crops up a great deal in this book, in the Lightning Process training, and my work as a whole. Therefore, it's worth clarifying at this point what I mean by it.

Looking this word up in the dictionary will give quite a confused list of definitions, ranging from the magical effects that stars were historically thought to have on people to the one we will be using in this book; the idea of being able to have an effect on some object or situation.

It's important to note that this concept differs from a number of other related terms such as:

- Blame
- Fault
- Responsibility

The difference being that 'influence' looks beyond who or what was to blame or at fault, and instead looks at what could be done to make things change.

So 'having an influence' means being someone who is going to do something about resolving a situation, by recognising the elements they can influence and then affecting those things to make a difference.

I often tell the following story about a bus journey to emphasise this important point.

Imagine we are on a bus, and whilst driving at speed down the road the bus driver suddenly falls into a coma and slumps over the wheel. This coma is because he is an insulin dependent diabetic and he hasn't taken his medication or eaten today, so his blood sugar levels have dropped to dangerous levels. Who is to blame and at fault for this situation?

Since the bus driver is in charge of monitoring and managing his blood sugar levels properly so he is competent to drive us safely, and he hasn't done that we could reasonably say that it's his fault for the situation that we, the passengers, now find ourselves in. His blood sugar levels aren't something we can really influence, so they are things that we are 'passive' to.

But who has an influence in potentially recovering the situation, for making it good and saving everyone?

The answer is of course anyone who can get to the wheel in time and take over the driving.

We could of course spend the remaining seconds of our lives blaming the bus driver as we head towards the oncoming traffic, but maybe there's more value in letting go of the idea of finding someone or something to blame and instead use that time more purposefully to rescue the situation.

One way of ensuring that things don't work out as planned is avoiding finding what elements you can influence, and instead spending as much time as possible finding out which people are to blame for things not working out. Useful targets for this are 'them' or 'the powers that be', 'men' or 'women', 'my partner', 'my parents' or 'my upbringing'.

It's probably true that all those things from your past that you feel are to blame for your current problems did have a negative effect on you. But does focusing on that actually make our current life any better, does it help us move on or does it just justify why things are the way they are and so hold everything in place?

Blaming is such a tempting idea that lures us when something goes wrong. I remember I once opened a cupboard in the kitchen, and a packet of open pretzels fell out and spilt right into my cup of tea. I began to curse everyone else in the house (in turn) for putting things in the cupboard in such a ridiculous way. Then I realised, everyone but me had gone away for the weekend. I had bought the pretzels and I was the only one who had been at home since the pretzels had been bought. I must have put them in the cupboard in such a ridiculous way. It was me - I did it. Notice how instantly I stepped into blame mode, finding a wrong doer, someone else to get annoyed and find fault with.

As Erica Jong said:

> *Take your life in your own hands and what happens? A terrible thing: no one is to blame.*

So to summarise, the concept of influence that I want to use, and for you to work with, throughout this book is not about fault-finding, and not even about thinking "I should have influenced that situation differently" (because that it just blaming yourself and of no use). Instead it's all about asking "What can I do about a situation to make it good or better?'

EXERCISE:
What will happen as you learn a new way to use that power you have to influence your life and take the driver's seat of your future?

The Long-term Success

We recognise that it is essential to carry out studies to scientifically verify the results we see in our seminars every day. We are currently in the advanced stages of planning randomised controlled trials with well established researchers, who are renowned within the research community, and who are assigned to acknowledged research institutes. The projects have been designed according to research standards as we feel this is essential for reliability and for acknowledgement.

Our filing cabinet is already bulging with cases, 'anecdotal' evidence, that supports the perspective that people can and do have lasting recovery. We have cards sent to us, by graduates of the LP seminars, from mountain tops all over the world that they have just climbed, photographs from shopping centres they have finally shopped in, from Christmas meals that they have finally been able to prepare and cook and of babies they have finally been able to have.

A logical consideration of what makes for long-term success will help us predict what is likely to happen to our successful participants. Let's go back to the idea of another training programme that we've mentioned before, one where you are going to learn French. It's similar to the Lightning Process in that the success an individual gains as a result of attending the training is dependent on:

1. The quality of the materials of the training
2. The quality of delivery of the training and support by the trainer
3. The degree of application by the participant

The successful student would choose a course that had been effective for other people, a trainer with the correct credentials and then would have to apply themselves effectively.

As a result they would learn the basics of French and we would consider that they have succeeded if they had the beginnings of fluency, but you wouldn't expect them to be able to read every single French word they came across. There would still be things to learn above and beyond the course but they could apply the basic skills they had discovered in their training - pronunciation, grammar, accent and how to find words in a dictionary etc.

So let's imagine that they leave the college with a good, sound grasp of French, but does that guarantee that they will speak French just as well, or even better, a year later? What do you think?

I would suggest that, no, you cannot guarantee that. At that point in their training the actual teaching part of the programme has stopped and the future is now in the hands of the participant. Has the programme provided them with the appropriate skills to start to master French? Yes. Has it provided them with the skills to be self-managing in their studies and have a good support network to assist them to put it into place? Yes. Is there much more the college can do, apart from locking them in the college to make sure they continue with their studies? At that point, the answer really has to be 'No'.

The college now takes on a much less influential role in the student's progression and the continuation of their usage of French. They are still available in a supporting role but now its primarily up to the student to use the tools and resources to keep their momentum.

In exactly the same way the Lightning Process is a training programme, the success at the end of the course can be clearly seen. The continued long-term success is dependent on the participant continuing to apply what they have learnt. Fortunately for us, as there is nothing more saddening than watching someone who has made major changes in their health and life, find themselves unable to keep up the training and changes, most of them do keep on applying the Process and continue to reap the rewards it can offer.

EXERCISE:
What does this teach you about what is required from you to get the best out of the Process?

What you get if you apply the Lightning Process to your life?

If after reading this book you decide to take the next step and take a Lightning Process seminar and apply it to your life, our experience tells us that you will get change in your life. And if you continue to apply it you'll begin to get the life you love.

The Way Forward

There will be many things for you to learn in this book, some of which will be obvious to you as you read it for the first time, although others will surface once your unconscious has begun to make sense of it all for you.

The Lightning Process suggests that you get out of life what you put in. So if you've got a life or health that are not as great as you'd like, it's time to discover if there is something you can do to influence that positively.

Whilst you read on, I suggest that you keep in mind what Henry Ford once said about success:

> *There are two types of people in the world, those who think they can, and those who think they can't - and they are both right.*

So, if you're ready for a change, let's continue.

Chapter 5
Foundations and Frameworks

Excellence

Much of my work over the last decade has focused on exactly how people do things excellently.

Let's begin by starting with a definition of 'excellence'. It could be described as "Consistent competence: the ability to reproduce the same expected results time and again".

EXCELLENCE (version 1) = consistently repeating expected results

When you ask an Olympic champion sprinter *how* does she run so fast, she'll probably reply, "I just do" or "I don't know". This is because, even though she excels in her sport, she's so familiar with doing it that she's forgotten *how* she reproduces her excellence consistently - she feels like she just does it.

This is very often true of experts. For example, many great scientists make appalling science teachers because they just can't understand how anyone could fail to grasp the basics of what they find so glaringly obvious. This perspective makes it very difficult for them to help others who are struggling to understand the basics of their subject, because it's been so long since they went through that process themselves.

Who do you think would make a better science teacher: someone who had struggled with science at school and then became an expert, or someone who seemed to be a natural born science genius?

Probably the one who struggled and then became an expert. They are more likely to be able to remember the steps of how they got to understand their subject, and so are more likely to be able to assist a struggling student in their class to work through the steps they need in order to master a particular topic.

The training and development programme I have undergone over the last twenty years has made me very skilled at being able to ask the right questions to understand in enough detail *how* people do things. This allows me to work out how that Olympic athlete actually does get that extra ounce of speed; this is technically called 'modelling'. Effective modelling is one important component of the Lightning Process.

Obviously our Olympic athlete's training regime, fitness levels, diet etc. are extremely important but most athletes deal with these issues and train in similar ways. In order to find out what makes the difference, what makes her excel, we need to understand other areas such as:

- Exactly *how* does she get herself out of bed to train early in the morning, every morning?
- *How* exactly does she stick to her diet?
- *How* does she manage to stay focused, even when the pressure's on?
- *How* does she deal with a race where she false starts or loses?
- *How* does she think as she lines up for a race, when she's lost the last two previous races, and goes on to lose that race too?
- *How* does she think as she lines up for a race, when she's lost the last three previous races and goes on to win that race?

And so on, but if we ask her these questions she probably won't know the answers as they are unlikely to be something she has much conscious awareness of.

In American football, soccer (called football in the UK) and rugby, there are moments of extreme tension when place/penalty kicks are taken. This is when play is stopped and one single player has the unenviable job of getting the ball through the goal posts or in football, past the goalkeeper. There is huge pressure on these kickers in these moments. Some of them are consistently brilliant (these are the highest paid ones!), however, other kickers are much more variable in their performance.

If you were choosing a team you'd want to select the ones that are able to perform no matter what. The ones who are able to kick well independent of whether:

- The team is winning or losing at that point in the game.
- The kick was being taken at his favourite end of the field or not.
- The entire outcome of the season/league/tournament or world cup is dependent upon the result of this kick.

The people who can do that are the top performers.

I've worked with top performers in various fields such as sport, music and business and although they are at the top of their field they are usually unaware of how they made their success happen. Often they will know some of the more obvious steps they took - the kicker knows he practised and understands how to place the ball and which leg to kick it with but they often don't know *how* they knew which steps to take, *how* they stayed motivated and *how* they stayed focused, etc.

This is because, although they are experts in their field, they are usually not experts in modelling.

The Lightning Process uses modelling in order to understand, in enough detail, *how* these experts do things. It means that I can take someone who wants to learn a particular set of skills and teach them how to emulate the success of top performers. On its own modelling won't make them an instantly top performer, they'll still have to put the hours in practising and preparing and do the work necessary to achieve their goals. But now they will know *what* work they need to do and *how* to approach that work like a champion. Lightning Process practitioners and very well trained advanced NLP practitioners are good at doing that, which means that we can help people develop in new areas and at rates which were often thought of as impossible.

A nice example of this was when some NLP practitioners were invited to work with the US army (Awaken the giant within, A Robbins 2001). The trainers were, not surprisingly, selected from the army's top marksmen, *the experts*. When these experts trained new recruits to shoot, only 70% passed the four-day pistol training. It had "always been this way" and so people just believed that "you were either a good shot (70%), or a poor shot (30%)."

The NLP team spent some time talking to the army's best shots. They began to 'model' these sharp shooters. They looked at all of the components: of *how* they thought about themselves, *how* they saw the target in their mind, *how* they held the pistol and so on in order to understand *how* these sharp shooters shoot so well.

They took this model of how to shoot well and taught it to new recruits in a one and a half day course. So rather than teaching them how to shoot, they taught them how to approach shooting like an expert. This time, even though the NLP trainers hadn't been trained to shoot, 100% of the recruits passed the course, and the quality of the marksmanship was so great that it produced three times as many 'expert level' shooters than the normal four day course.

Again, the sharp shooting *experts* who taught at the pistol range were great at shooting, but because they found it easy and because they were expert marksmen rather than experts at modelling they didn't actually know the basic steps of *how* they got to be so good. This meant that they found it difficult to teach others.

This leads us to expand on our basic definition of 'excellence.' Initially we described it as: 'consistent competence: the ability to reproduce the same expected results time and again'.

EXCELLENCE (version 1) = consistently repeating expected results

Now it can be more completely stated as: 'consistent competence: the ability to reproduce the same expected results time and again, unconsciously and automatically'.

EXCELLENCE (version 2) = consistently repeating expected results, unconsciously and automatically

Transferring Skills

The whole purpose of understanding excellence is to identify enough of the key components of that excellence, so that we can have a chance to teach someone how to effectively emulate the success of a star performer. There are many reasons why this very reasonable and useful process isn't that commonly practiced; the most important is that most people think that those who are great at something are great at it because *they just are* - that it's part of their fortune, their make-up, their luck.

As Thomas Jefferson said:

> *I am a great believer in luck. I find that the harder I work the more luck I seem to have.*

The following story about skiing comes from the incorrect belief that excellence is just a god-given gift and that some things are just not able to be taught. Some people believe that if you're born with it you have it and if not then that's just tough. No matter what you do, you will never be that good at it.

Skiing

Many years ago, before skiing was the popular sport that it is now, skiing was a skill that was only found in certain remote communities in parts of the world where there was snow a large proportion of the time. During those times of the year the only reasonable form of transport was skiing.

By necessity, people from these remote villages had to become very adept at using skis to avoid being cut off during the snowy season. When strangers came to those villages and attempted to use this unfamiliar form of transport they found that they just couldn't make the skis work. This was partly due to a lack of experience, a lack of skilled teaching and sometimes an unwillingness of the community to educate the stranger into their very special skills.

The strangers discovered this bizarre form of transport was impossible to use and concluded that this must be due to the fact they just didn't have the innate ability. As more and more people discovered that they were unable to learn to ski, whilst the villagers found it easy, the more they became convinced that it was just one of those things that the people in these villages had a genetic disposition for. If you hadn't been born into that kind of village, or didn't share that gene pool, then it was just one of those things you couldn't do.

This belief was held for a long time because when anybody tried to learn and found they couldn't, it provided more evidence to support this belief. It was many years before people started to have the time, exposure and inclination to be able to assess and understand exactly what went on when somebody successfully skied and only then could people begin to emulate the success of these apparently naturally genetic skiers.

When we now look back at this scenario it seems ridiculous. How could people ever have believed that skiing was a genetically inherited talent? But much of our history is littered with once universal and now discarded concepts. When these ideas were thought to be true there were often many obstacles that prevented any closer examination of them to discover if they really were accurate. For instance:

In the 16th Century, the established (Christian) church said that the earth was the centre of the universe, which was based on their interpretation of the scriptures. To say otherwise was a heresy punishable by death. This did not encourage people to investigate whether it's true or not. Nicolaus Copernicus (1473-1543) thought that the earth being the centre of the universe didn't fit with his observations of the movements of the planets and stars and suggested that the earth revolved around the sun. There are a number of versions as to what happened next, some say he was forced to publicly disown his findings to avoid charges of heresy, others that he waited until his death to publish his major work.

In our exploration of excellence, we have found all kinds of things that have often been thought of as innate abilities, or god-given gifts, but that are actually able to be taught. For instance, by studying excellent spellers we can teach people who've had spelling dyslexia all their lives to spell consistently in about ten minutes. If that challenges your beliefs about spelling and spelling dyslexia then you have a choice:

- To discount it as rubbish, knowing from your personal experience that that's just not possible as you've tried to help people/yourself with spelling issues and never achieved that result. To do this you must also deny the experience of thousands of ex-bad spellers who can now spell perfectly.
- Or you might consider, if it is true (and it is), what must be different about our approach that makes it so successful? I think of it like DIY. If you try and put up some shelves using only a pencil you'll get limited results. Adding a hammer to your toolbox may not be enough. You might need a screwdriver, a spirit level and a drill, to get the job done properly. If you don't have the effective tools for teaching good spelling it will be difficult to *consistently* help people to become good spellers. However, if you do, it becomes much simpler.

We've also looked at many other excellences. For example, studying fast readers means we can teach slow readers to read at high speed.

The Lightning Process has looked at success in many different fields and has begun to discover a consistency amongst top performers: the way they approach life, the way they operate and the way they think. Once these patterns have been identified, they can be taught using the Lightning Process.

Health and Excellence

This is one of the many core applications of the Process, but the effects of such changes in the way your brain works doesn't just impact your level of success. It fundamentally changes the way your brain operates which can have a startlingly positive impact on your health too. Having read the section on placebos this should come as no surprise to you. Later in the book I will outline some of the mechanisms of how our body influences our brain function and how our brain influences our body. It's worth considering at this point, as our health is influenced by the way our brain operates and the way our brain works is influenced by our health, if we could learn *how* people with great health think, what might be possible for us?

EXERCISE:

When you've resolved whatever is stopping you from having a great life, what would you love to learn to do even better?

Looking at the ideas about success above, what kinds of skills would you like to learn from people who are already successful in your chosen field?

The Lightning Process Building Blocks

I designed the Lightning Process using ideas, philosophies and skills from a number of different fields. The following is a brief description of some of the major areas that influenced its creation.

Osteopathy

Osteopathy was originally designed by AT Still, a doctor and pastor who lived in the southern states of the USA. He grew up in the 1830s, in relatively rural surroundings, so it was through necessity that he developed a strong interest and aptitude in engineering and mechanics. It was these skills that were to be important in the development of osteopathy.

After the death of three of his children from spinal meningitis, which the medicine of his time had failed to cure, he concluded that the orthodox medical practices of his day were frequently ineffective and sometimes harmful. He therefore, spent the next ten years of his life studying the human body, paying particular attention to anatomy, physiology, mechanics and psychology, constantly working towards finding better ways to treat disease. As AT Still said:

> *Osteopathy is a science which consists of such exact exhaustive and verifiable knowledge of the structure and functions of the human mechanism, anatomy, physiology and psychology... (that by using) resources within the body by scientific treatment peculiar to osteopathic practice... (the body) may recover from displacements, derangements, disorganizations and consequent diseases and regain its normal equilibrium of form and function in health and strength.*

From his studies he introduced the concept of 'the lesion' which became one of the cornerstones of osteopathy. The basis was that once the body had deviated from its original design blueprint (i.e. was 'in lesion'), it could no longer function as intended and some degree of dysfunction and illness was sure to follow. The osteopath's job was therefore, to discover this lesion, or deviation from the norm, and to correct it. A simple way of thinking about 'the lesion' is to substitute it with the phrase 'a bit out of place'. He also put forward other key concepts including:

- Areas of lesion in one place will have an effect on the body as a whole.
- Structure and function are interdependent (a lesion will cause problems/issues and problems/issues will cause a lesion).
- There is a self-healing mechanism operating within the body.

Many people think that osteopathy is just a physical approach to moving bones about and helping bad backs but this is a modern distortion and a watering down of what Still and the other ground breaking osteopaths who came after him had in mind. Still's idea of the lesion was expanded further by

Littlejohn, a physiologist as well as an osteopath. He encouraged osteopaths to consider if a person was in lesion or at odds with their environment. This substantially widened the scope of osteopathic attention from solely considering the body as their domain to including more distant factors such as working environment, pollution and diet as possible causes of ill health.

Dynamic Osteopath Technique forms part of the theory behind the Lightning Process and continues this osteopathic development of the idea of the lesion. It considers not just the person's structure or the relationship between them and their environment but also the relationship between the person and themselves. Are they in lesion with themselves, the life they would love to be living and their life's purpose? Fixing these lesions clearly requires a different approach than fixing lesions in the spine.

In the 1950s, osteopathic researchers began to use the term 'facilitation' to explain how osteopathy worked. Facilitation is a state of affairs where a part of the body has become so 'in lesion' (or wonky) that it starts to send signals to the nervous system about how everything is going wrong with it. Because it's not working very well, sometimes these signals can also be messed up and it is difficult for the nervous system to understand. It's like a child who's desperately upset trying to explain what's wrong by yelling, stamping and crying.

The nervous system responds as best as it can to these signals that it's receiving from the lesioned part, but sometimes the signals request it to do the opposite to what is actually needed (like a child shouting "GO AWAY!", when they really want a hug). This sets up what is called a positive feedback cycle, where the problem (the lesion) now creates a response (from the nervous system) which worsens the problem (the lesion). In this facilitated state, anything that happens near or around the lesioned area creates a larger than necessary and unhealthy response, which further sets off the destructive positive feedback cycle. Until that loop is broken, ill heath and poor function will prevail.

The Lightning Process is an excellent way of intervening with this damaging state of affairs, and restores order and calm to facilitation; whether it be just on a small scale 'sore back' level, a 'getting stressed, guts spasms and sweating at the thought of meeting new people' or a 'whole body in a state of chaos' situation.

A final word on Dr Still. He was a visionary in medicine who promoted, about a century before orthodox medicine, the idea of preventive medicine and endorsed the philosophy that physicians should focus on treating the entire patient, rather than just the disease. In many ways the Lightning Process, which I named it in the late nineties, would never have been designed if it wasn't for his ideas together with my training and lecturing experience as an osteopath. As I wrote this book I came across a reference to something I'd learnt long ago as an undergraduate but had forgotten until now; one of his earliest descriptions of himself and his work was as a 'lightning bone setter' - it's funny how things can work sometimes!

Neuro-Linguistic Programming (NLP)

NLP is an offshoot of hypnotherapy and psychotherapy and was developed by doctors Bandler and Grinder after they had studied the major proponents of therapy (Perls, Satir, Erickson et al). It is a system for finding out in detail how individuals achieve excellence, using the modelling process we looked at earlier. The modelling process is complete when enough detail has been discovered to teach that excellence to a novice and help them to achieve excellence in that field.

NLP has modelled many excellences such as spelling, speed reading and sharp shooting (discussed earlier) and is ideally suited to helping recreate peak performance in any field. It also looks at what makes a great therapeutic intervention asking such questions as:

- How did those people get over that horrific event in their life?
- How did those people find such a profound level of happiness in their life?

This has resulted in a therapeutic use for NLP, which achieves extraordinarily deep and fast results for people with even the most complex issues.

I designed the Lightning Process when I found that these tried and tested skills that were usually successful, didn't produce the results I expected. Although it incorporates some elements of NLP, the LP is not 'just another version of NLP'.

Life Coaching

Life coaching is an approach to help others get the most out of themselves and to achieve what they are truly capable of. A key part of its philosophy is that the coach's role is less one of giving advice and much more one of helping the person being coached to discover the questions they need to ask themselves to uncover the resources and solutions inside themselves. This philosophy underpins the training and usage of the Lightning Process.

Does it involve Hypnosis?

I quite often get asked the interesting question "Is hypnosis part of the Lightning Process?" The simple answer is 'No'.

Many people's concerns about 'hypnosis' are about someone potentially taking control of them. I think this is something one should rightly be very concerned about. Having said that I should point out that although this idea of 'being under someone else's control' is one of the commonly held myths about hypnosis it is not actually true and is based more on the questionable values and skills of Stage Hypnotism shows and Hollywood movies rather than modern clinical hypnotherapy.

I would always recommend that you should avoid letting anyone take control of your life or choices. The Lightning Process, in fact, focuses a great deal on how you can start to make better choices in your life, helping you to discover what's important for you and finding ways to move your life forward by using your own innate abilities.

So you can rest assured that if you don't want to engage in any programme which tells you what to do or takes control of you, then the Lightning Process is something that will suit you very well.

Religious Beliefs

Another concern that is often raised is whether the training will conflict with any religious beliefs a participant might have. In my experience we have seen people from all of the worlds main religions: Hindus, Muslims, Christians (spanning a broad range from Evangelical, Catholic, Church of England, Jehovah's Witnesses, etc.), Jews and Buddhists. Not only did the Process not conflict with their religious beliefs and practices but they found the conceptual similarities of certain elements of the training helped to strengthen and deepen their individual faith.

Chapter 6
The PER and the Destructive Spiral

This chapter explains two of the key concepts of the LP - the Physical Emergency Response and the Destructive Spiral. Learning about this will make it easier to understand how people became so stuck in their lives and health and how, through using the LP, they were finally able to break through that stuckness.

The information that follows is a relatively brief introduction to the subject, but it is discussed in much more detail during the LP seminar.

How can a non-drug, or medical based approach, like the LP help you influence your body's health?

This is something that many people are initially confused about which isn't surprising as the answer only becomes clear when you have a fairly in-depth understanding of how the human body works.

Physical Emergency Response (PER)

This is when the body experiences an emergency or threat to its safety and well-being, which could include:

- Physical injury or extreme environmental conditions, such as burning or freezing etc.
- Poisoning, due to viruses, alcohol, bad food, drug reactions etc.
- Emotional shock and trauma

The body then naturally produces the PER to deal with the threat and to find a way to recover or stay safe.

There are a number of key ways the PER affects the body. It stimulates the sudden:

- Activation of one particular part of the nervous system called the the Sympathetic Nervous System

- Production of some very powerful hormones called adrenaline, nor adrenaline, dopamine, cortisol and dehydroepiandrosterone (DHEA)

This is exactly what needs to happen to help us deal with the threat. The PER does this by primarily giving our muscles an extra burst of speed and strength and affecting the nervous system's synapses and their neurotransmitters. Temporarily this is an excellent solution for dealing with most threats, but unfortunately long term arousal of this system has been long known to have a detrimental effect on many other body systems, and this causes disruption to normal immune, muscle and digestive system function (see below) and changes the way our nerve cells transmit nerve signals.

The Immune System

The immune system is a key system of the body that has an important role in supporting the way all other body systems work. It has many important functions, including recognising, dealing with and removing:

- Infections
- Foreign materials
- Toxins
- Old, worn out or bad functioning cells

There are two possible extremes of immune dysfunction:

1. Low functioning immune system, resulting in:
    a) An inability to clear infections
    b) Poor detoxification (leading to poisoning) of all body tissues with resulting poor function of all body systems
    c) Inability to distinguish foreign matter from it's own components and 'bad' cells from good

2. Over active, out of control immune system, resulting in:
    a) Inability to distinguish foreign matter from it's own components and 'bad' cells from good – concluding

with attacks directed at own, well functioning tissue (auto-immune issues)

b) Wastage of body resources

As you can see from this list, any problems in this important system will have an effect throughout all the other body systems.

The Muscular System

Osteopathy has always had a strong focus on the importance of the muscular system, especially as it is the main user of energy in the body. As a result much of the body's support systems (blood, waste disposal, communications) are dedicated to keeping the muscles working well.

When the muscles don't work well, not only can we no longer move ourselves about as we would want to, it also puts an added strain on these core support systems. As movement itself is vital for pumping blood in the veins and fluid in the tissues back towards the heart, poor movement puts more strain on the heart and circulatory systems.

Again as you can see from this any problems with the muscular system have an impact throughout all other body systems.

The Digestive System

This system has a number of important functions. The most obvious is, of course, to bring nutrition into the body; any problems in this system will have a major effect everywhere else.

Its other functions include a role:

- In the immune system, protecting the body from invading organisms that gain entry through our food/gut
- In removing wastes and toxins

The Nervous System

This includes the brain, spinal cord and all the nerves of the body. Their primary job is to ensure that there is good communication between the brain and all areas of the body in both directions. In something as complex as our bodies any small disruptions in the way this very sensitive system works can have massive consequences.

Destructive Spiral

Having understood the PER and the importance of these systems, this allows us to make sense of the destructive spiral or as we also call it, the 'Physiological Catch 22'. This is one of the important elements of the Lightning Process. It came from having discussions with thousands of people with many chronically stuck conditions about the course of their illness. In these discussions I found they had experienced some variation of the following downward spiral.

1. Exactly how the problem started was often different from one individual to another – but frequently included responses to viruses, operations, vaccines, or even emotional stress. This onset 'event', whatever its cause, is seen as a threat by the body.

2. This threat, as discussed above, causes a PER. The PER stimulates the Sympathetic Nervous System and the production of adrenaline, noradrenaline, dopamine, cortisol and DHEA. These changes powerfully affect our blood pressure, sugar levels, thyroid levels and many key body systems.

3. This means the body is now having to deal with a combination of physical changes and threats:
   - The effects of the original 'event' are now combined with:
     - The direct effects of the symptoms
     - And the effects of the PER

4. In some cases, for various reasons which are not always clear, this combination of threats and changes produces an increased and prolonged PER. This long-term stimulation of this system (which is described in the chapter 13) has a detrimental effect on the way the immune, muscular, digestive and nerve signal transmission systems and many other body systems function.

5. Any disruption to the immune system in particular makes any healing more difficult. This takes the body back to step 2 again creating a downward health spiral.

This spiral can be further worsened by the added effect of the emotional distress of being unwell and all the questions and uncertainties that can raise about ones future.

When viewed with this understanding of some of the physical processes that go on as a response to ill health, it becomes clear that a training programme, such as the LP, which teaches you how to influence these physical processes, can open up a route to recovery from serious physical or psychological illness.

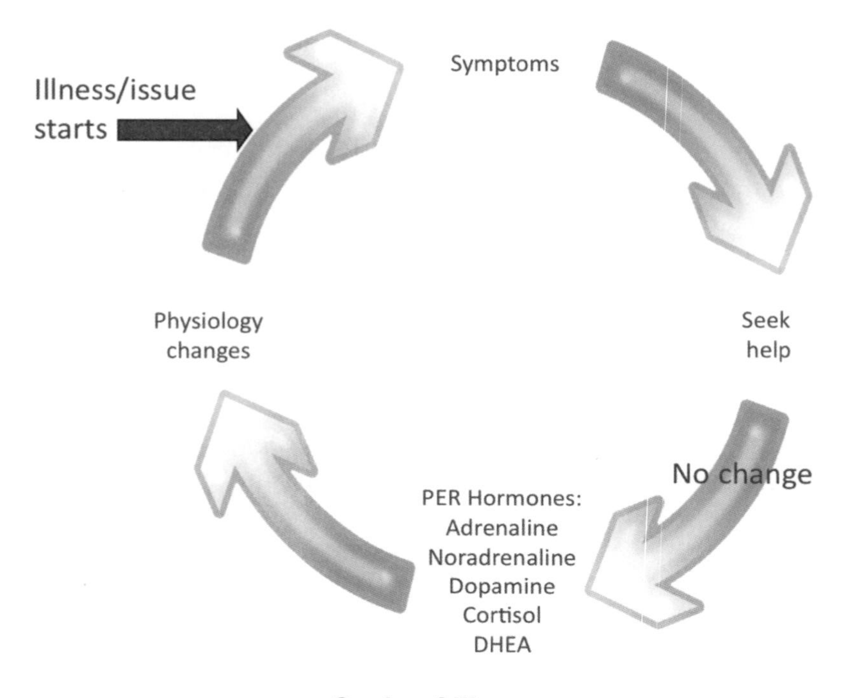

Cycle of illness

Does the LP lower levels of adrenaline and cortisol?

Having read the previous explanation it might lead you to think that the Lightning Process is a method for *reducing* adrenaline - but this is actually a simplification of quite a complex situation. In fact in some cases this long-term, over-stimulation of the PER and its related hormone system adds a further level of complexity to that PER/illness cycle. The over-production can then lead to an exhaustion of the glands that produce the hormones resulting in unusually low levels of these important hormones. This can have a different but equally damaging affect on the body.

In fact, although adrenaline, cortisol and the other hormones released by the PER are important in many, but not all conditions, it is not an over production of these hormones, but a dysregulation i.e. poor regulation, that is the key problem.

The physiology can become even more complicated. Due to the way that the various hormonal systems within the body interrelate, a dysfunctional production of one hormone almost invariably creates an effect on other hormones' production.

In CFS/ME for example, research shows that in some cases you can see high levels of adrenaline and cortisol, in others low levels and in some there are huge fluctuations of the levels. Considering that:

- Adrenaline is thought to have a half-life of between eighteen seconds and two minutes (depending on which authority you consult), which means that every eighteen seconds (or two minutes) half of the adrenaline that's racing around your bloodstream will have been used up, excreted, removed or destroyed.
- Adrenaline production depends hugely on physical strains and perceptions of threats from moment to moment.

This means that accurately measuring the levels is always going to be hard to do and that a reading will only be valid for a brief period of time.

The key word in all of this is dysregulation, which brings us back to our osteopathic philosophy; 'when the body isn't doing what it's designed to do, something won't work properly as a result'. In order to have good body function we need to improve the regulation of the production of these powerful hormones.

And finally it's also important to keep in mind that although this is a very influential physiological problem, the destructive spiral is just one of the elements of some illnesses and not the only factor addressed in the LP.

Chapter 7
CFS/ME and Other Similar Conditions

CFS/ME is an abbreviation for:
Myalgic Encephalopathy/Chronic Fatigue Syndrome.

For those of you with CFS/ME and similar conditions

The Lightning Process has become something of a fascinating issue in the press and media over recent years, particularly because of the extraordinary success it's had in dealing with the appallingly debilitating condition, CFS/ME. As a result, a number of you will probably be skipping straight to this chapter to start your journey to join the ranks of the thousands who have found solutions to their CFS/ME by using the Lightning Process. I wouldn't recommend that – as you will miss out some of the important elements that will make this chapter easier to understand. Instead please read the book from the start, it will work better that way.

For those of you without CFS/ME

Some of you might feel that you can skip this chapter because you don't have CFS/ME or other similar health issues. I wouldn't recommend that either. As I mentioned in the introduction, these stories are a powerful demonstration of how even the most debilitated and apparently hopeless cases can be resolved simply and rapidly using the Process. The question I would ask you to hold in mind is, "If these people with CFS/ME have resolved their difficulties, then what can I do with mine?"

Similar Conditions

There are a number of other illnesses that are useful to discuss at the same time as CFS/ME. This is not because they are all the same illnesses, but because in my experience they have similar underlying pathological processes, and all respond equally well to the LP. These include:

- Fibromyalgia (FM)
- Post Viral Syndrome (PVS)

- Glandular Fever (GF)

What is CFS/ME?

CFS/ME is a disabling neurological illness that has confused the medical profession for years. They have had a very difficult time treating CFS/ME because from their perspective they've found:

- No agreed diagnostic test
- No consistent findings in all cases
- No consistent virus or bacteria found in all cases

Worst of all, as far as main-stream medicine is concerned, there appears to be no effective cure. Time seems to heal but the progress is slow, up and down and impossible to predict.

Based on this history and anecdotal evidence on how difficult it is to recover from CFS/ME, the rapid and lasting success that other sufferers have achieved by using the Lightning Process, is often met with scepticism and downright disbelief.

Like many complementary health practitioners working in the 1980s, I felt sure I had a great deal to offer clients with CFS/ME but as time went by I found that although I could help them a bit, I struggled to help them maintain their improvements. After a while I began to almost dread new CFS/ME clients as it was so unsatisfying and upsetting to have to stand by helplessly seeing them continue to suffer.

After developing the Lightning Process, and finding it so successful with all sorts of 'difficult to treat' cases, I began treating CFS/ME sufferers once again. To my astonishment the effects were instant and profound. Participants with all kinds of different CFS/ME symptoms got better overnight. At first I was cautious of the initial success, would it last? Did it just work for a few people and had I just been lucky with my first clients?

After seeing many CFS/ME clients who all reported the same dramatic improvements and had experienced a complete remission from all their symptoms, I followed them up over the following four-year period and I discovered three important things:

1. CFS/ME can be turned around rapidly.
2. The Lightning Process is an effective approach for rapidly and permanently recovering from CFS/ME.
3. There is a set of common findings in all CFS/ME cases that we have examined so far.

CFS/ME isn't in the mind

You might think from reading this book that I'd be the kind of person that might say that CFS/ME is in the mind, but I don't think it is. I think it's a real, true and genuinely physical condition.

One of the greatest fears of many sufferers of CFS/ME is that people will think or assume that they are just malingering (which they are not) and that there isn't anything wrong with them and they should just stop pretending to be ill. This is heightened by medicine's inability to find anything consistently wrong with them.

The idea therefore, of trying a training programme that has a track record of helping some issues that stem from the workings of the mind is often the last thing they want to contemplate, surely this will just confirm what some people have been saying about them not really being 'properly ill'. So for those of you suffering from CFS/ME or similar conditions let me outline how I view these medical conditions and syndromes within the context of the Lightning Process. If any of this seems unfamiliar or challenges any beliefs you currently have then that is a good thing. It's important when creating change to be able to start to look at things differently.

I also feel that although it's a physical condition, physical cures like osteopathy, nutrition, pacing and rest are helpful to some degree but they are simply not very effective in producing rapid, effective and lasting recovery. Therefore, if what you are doing is ineffective it's time to try something else. If you're having trouble getting your head around this, consider the Sherlock Holmes axiom:

> *When you have eliminated the impossible, whatever remains, however improbable, must be the truth.*

Many people consult me with other physical conditions that just won't resolve using normal methods including back pain, headaches, paralysis, asthma, eczema, digestive problems and allergies. In these cases and in the case of CFS/ME the solution is to work with the way our body and brain interact with our neuromuscular, endocrinal and immunological systems. A large part of the first day of the Lightning Process training consists of explanation and discussion of the mechanisms and pathophysiology that underlie how CFS/ME begins and is maintained.

Ruth's Story

> *I am so glad to have this opportunity to express the immense joy I feel in having been completely cured of CFS/ME in quite literally minutes, using Phil Parker's Lightning Process. My experience of CFS/ME had been extremely severe. I cannot say when it started for the build-up of stress and symptoms were insidious throughout my teenage years, but by the age of twenty I was completely bedbound for twenty-four hours a day.*
>
> *My parents diagnosed me after weeks of anxious studying. Many remedies were tried with hugely detrimental results and there was no real help from the NHS. I declined rapidly into a vegetative like state and was fed, washed and turned over daily by my parents who gave up their retirement to care for me. I struggled to retain my consciousness as I felt in agony, buried alive with excruciating pain. I lost my ability to speak and couldn't tolerate the brightness of any sunlight. In some ways I was fortunate in that I was too ill to become depressed although it was six years before I could begin to speak again and start to ask for help.*

Three years ago when I was almost twenty six, I started an antioxidant protocol formulated and administered by a South African doctor and at last I began to improve a little. After three years of this I felt able to seek help outside of my home and bedroom, although I was still horizontal most of the day at this point.

I spoke to Phil Parker and he told me about the seemingly amazing results he'd got by using the Lightning Process to help others with similar problems to me. I started the Process in October and within minutes I knew there was no possibility of staying ill any longer! The effect was immediate. Phil shone a light on the 'condition' and upon me which allowed me to see for the first time what CFS/ME really is. Phil taught me how to clearly see a way out for myself.

It's now been three days since my first day of training and I have been cured for two whole days. I am at long last experiencing a truly energetic and dynamic existence. What I've been able to do physically for the last forty-eight hours is so exciting as I've been up with the dawn and busy all day, not going to bed till very late evening and enjoying every moment, relishing every new discovery.

I feel the Lightning Process has 'uncovered' me and now I can see myself and my own desires and ambitions - I can find my place in the world. This is so much more than just a cure for ME! It's the gift of a real human life; how we are designed to live, in the truth and spontaneity of ourselves within the present moment. For me anyway, the Lightning Process has re-taught me how to live a jubilant existence therefore, with great joy I want to exclaim "Thank you Phil!"

Ruth's story continues:

Due to an extreme reaction to the damp and spores in her parent's house, Ruth had been unable to visit her parents, or even see them, unless they were wearing clothes that had never been inside the family home. She wrote this a month after her first visit:

> *I have now been able to spend over an hour with my parents in their home - my family and friends are absolutely thrilled. I can't express how amazing this is, thank you.*

A year later, Ruth completed a walk along the Northumbrian Coastal path.

Evelyn's Story:

> *When I was forty-three I was struck down by the debilitating symptoms and restricted lifestyle imposed by CFS/ME. Initially I had been very severely affected but even though more recently things had improved a bit, I still spent most days on the sofa or bed and was only able to leave the house for a few hours, at most once a week, relying on my wheelchair for outside mobility.*
>
> *Although like many others I found this hard to accept and had tried to regain my health nothing provided the answers for which I yearned and the cure remained elusive for twelve years. That was until by chance, at the age of fifty-five, I heard about Phil Parker and his Lightning Process. Having read Ruth's testimonial and then checking out Phil's website, I felt inspired to phone for more information. Within the hour I had made the necessary appointment with him.*
>
> *The first session covered so much ground about how I had got and stayed so unwell - everything I learnt in that session made so much sense and was precisely in keeping with the way I was beginning to view the illness. That session also taught me the tools to recover.*

That afternoon I went shopping with my husband for hours. I decided I wouldn't need my wheelchair - not only on that day, but ever again. When I got home that evening I stayed up for hours, later than I had in years.

Today is day two of the Process and I have turned my back on CFS/ME forever. I have the tools now to know that I can free myself from it's vice-like grip.

I already regard myself as having recovered and the future glows brilliantly ahead of me. It's amazing! Now I am in control of my life. I really feel I have come alive!

Evelyn phoned a week later to add:

When we last spoke I created a list of things to do as a measure of my ability to function normally. Well I'm pleased to report that I have done all the things on my list and friends, family and neighbours have all noticed that I'm looking different and am much calmer.

I've also noticed that I've been able to be so much more spontaneous. I've been to places that have been off limits to me for years as they're not wheelchair accessible. Thanks Phil.

Evelyn sent us this after a month:

Well, one month on and I'm delighted to say that my progress continues. After all these years I am having difficulty staying indoors and now go out twice most days! The freedom and pleasure of being around other people is overwhelming.

It is also wonderful to be able to spend more time with my husband who has been a great support to me. We are now returning to a more equal relationship and I feel that I can begin to take much of the load off his shoulders. We have such plans for the future, and he says he feels like he has a new wife!

I am rapidly regaining my confidence and independence - driving and socialising once more. Oh, the thrill of having a really good long chat with a friend! My legs are getting stronger too and I now cope easily with supermarket shopping. Housework is also a joy, which of course leaves my husband extra time for those DIY tasks.

Roll on summer - oh to go on holiday again! The only problem is... where to go first?

Evelyn wrote in with this after three months:

Well Phil, I'm so sorry that this update on my recovery has taken such a long time to arrive, as you've no doubt guessed I've been really busy!

Amazingly this morning I mowed the lawn! Really, was that me? I've also had a walk in the park and completed a supermarket shop. The list goes on, what a wonderful day and my life continues to improve. For half a day a week now I do some voluntary work and it's so good to feel of use to others once more.

When my father was recently in hospital I was able to visit him twice a day and at last feel that I can resume my role as a supportive daughter. Needless to say he is delighted with my progress too. My birthday also arrived and instead of spending it with the TV, I had a meal out in the evening with dear friends and had a wonderful time.

In the early days of CFS/ME I felt that I was living a nightmare and hoped to wake up for a better life. Now I am living that life.

Interestingly, Evelyn's son also had CFS/ME. He'd watched his mum's initial excitement with some scepticism and her continued improvement with growing interest but for his own reasons decided it wasn't for him. We hear this quite often. In fact, many of our participants tell us that they wouldn't have been seen dead trying out something as 'un-orthodox' as the Lightning Process only months before they decided to take the training, but that someone's story on the website or someone they know personally both before, during and after the Process, somehow gives them a change of heart.

Two years later, almost to the day, having found he was once again struggling with his energy at university, he too decided to learn the Process. Like his mother, within the first day of the training, his CFS/ME went and he now maintains a full and normal undergraduate life.

Sarah's Story

I'd had CFS/ME for five and a half years when I came across Phil Parker's Lightning Process in a book I was reading. The book detailed how it had been successful in 'curing' two people of CFS/ME. Since being diagnosed with CFS/ME, I'd spent a lot of time, money and effort in searching for a cure. I'd tried everything from conventional medicine and alternative therapies to the bizarre! Conventional medicine didn't help, although a supportive GP was invaluable. Reflexology, Acupuncture, Tai Chi and psychotherapy worked for me but although I made good progress I couldn't seem to achieve full recovery no matter how dedicated I was.

When I booked my training with Phil, I was scared; if this didn't work, I felt I had nowhere left to go. Before my first session with Phil I was having nine to ten hours of restless sleep a night and resting a lot in the day due to un-refreshing sleep. I had only enough energy to work a couple of hours a week for a local charity and avoided most social occasions due to fear of not being well enough. I was also fearful of pushing myself in case my symptoms worsened and spent most of my day anxious about being ill.

After the first session I felt different. I was more self-confident and for the first time in five years I was confident that my body was going to fully recover, and I felt stronger. By the end of the second session I was no longer feeling tired or dizzy and was able to go for a long walk in the evening after a day spent walking around the city.

I left after my third session free of CFS/ME and committed to regaining my former physical strength and a life that I loved.

A week on from my first session, and I'm walking ninety minutes a day. I'm also doing two days a week voluntary work and have attended a yoga class and two Tai Chi classes in the last three days. I've also been socialising with astonished friends and family who have been complimenting me on how well I look. In addition, I've been doing the shopping, cooking and housework. I am getting eight hours of refreshing sleep a night and I'm happy and positive and life is fun and easy again. I could never have imagined how quickly and by how much the Process could change things for me. I was sceptical before booking my training about how effective the Process would be and I did think that it might not work for me but I was so wrong.

I know I will go from strength to strength and my goal now is to be fitter than I was previous to having CFS/ME. I can't thank Phil enough for teaching me how to reclaim my life.

Two weeks later she wrote:

My life continues to improve. I drove home from the train station on Thursday - the longest distance I have driven in four years (and in the dark). I spent all day Friday and Saturday driving around, going out for lunch, shopping etc.

Today I've been to do my voluntary work, walked two hours and I've done a two hour Tai Chi class! I'm so pleased. Thanks again.

Ten months later she wrote:

It is ten months to the day since I had my first session with Phil. Looking back, I hardly recognise the life I was living then and I'm truly thankful to Phil for the profound changes he has helped me make.

Over this time I have started two part time jobs (working both of them for the last six months) and I started a college course five months ago. I exercise every day, I spend weekends socialising and I'm in the process of buying a house. Ten months ago, even considering one of these things would have sent me into a panic and yet now I am able to keep my life in balance for the first time. After curing myself of CFS/ME, I was curious to see what other changes I was able to make.

The changes I experienced as a result of using it on other issues were the most profound of all. I have changed at a fundamental level and have achieved the change that I had always wanted but until I met Phil had no idea how I was going to achieve. It has affected every area of my life. It has enhanced all the other changes I have made and it has enriched and continues to enrich my whole experience of life.

The great thing about how the Lightning Process works is that you can take it as far as you need/want to. The tools are there - you can decide what masterpiece you create!

Three years later:

She has now completed her college training and is working full time. She continues to be well.

Claire's story:

Claire's life and her career in the city were stopped dead in their tracks when she developed CFS/ME. She tells the story of her recovery in her own words:

Day dreaming about socialising, exercising, having a career and just generally having fun was what I did most days when I had CFS/ME. Actually being able to do these things seemed like a faraway dream.

I had CFS/ME for two years and every time I thought I was finally regaining my health I would relapse, leaving me feeling like I would never again be the lively person I once was. Some days even getting out of bed and walking around the garden for ten minutes was a struggle.

Also, food for me was a huge issue. Every month I seemed to become intolerant to something. Of course I had been to see all the top consultants in the field and tried osteopathy and massage therapy but even though their treatments seemed to work short term, the effects failed to last. Each time I was left feeling frustrated and miserable. I was 100 percent committed to recovery so why wasn't I getting any results?

I have now realised that the power to heal myself has always been within me, instead of looking to external medication and therapies for a cure.

After doing the Lightning Process for just three days, I have walked for forty minutes everyday, had a friend round for five hours solid and eaten apple pie and spicy food! My muscles feel supple and loose and most importantly I have had no rest periods and I am sleeping soundly during the night!

I'm even planning a trip to Newcastle - something that I would have been far too scared to do just a few days ago! My friends and family are shocked at my sudden health and energy but for me it feels so natural to be doing so much again and I can now look forward to my future.

I would urge you to give the Lightning Process a chance as it has enabled me to regain my health. I am so thankful to Phil who has taught me how to get my life back.

Claire emailed us two weeks later with this update:

I just thought I'd let you know that last night I went out in Covent Garden for the first time in two years and it was amazing!

I had such a cool time and I was even drinking (not to excess though, I alternated between vodka, champagne and gallons of water) and I didn't collapse and die or anything! I danced all night long and when the bar closed at two-ish, I wanted to carry on somewhere else, unfortunately no one else did! Wow, I'm just so happy I had to share it with you!

Many people who use the Lightning Process to completely turn their health or life around, feel that now they've got their life back they want to do something powerful, contributing and fulfilling with it. After experiencing the life changing effects of this work for themselves and being amazed with what's possible, a few of them, unsurprisingly decide that this is a path they want to follow. Having used the Process on themselves they can speak with authority on the power of the mind to create problems and solutions and therefore, make excellent practitioners as a result.

In our London clinic we currently have two practitioners who both had very severe long-term CFS/ME which they recovered from using the Lightning Process - Claire is one of them.

These are just a handful of cases out of the many we have collected, but they are typical. Our experience is if they can do it by following the steps of the Process then why should you not expect yourself to get exactly the same kinds of results? For more inspirational stories and photographs please visit the website **www.lightningprocess.com/CFS-ME-home/**

EXERCISE:
What have I learned by reading these case histories?

1.
2.
3.
4.

Same and Different

One of the commonest patterns of thinking that we have seen in virtually every case is something I've called the 'Same and Different' pattern.

I was made very aware of it one day after working with a group of CFS/ME sufferers. At the end of their Lightning Process training they had all left their CFS/ME far behind and were discussing what obstacles they had encountered when deciding to come on the course in the first place.

One participant said that she had watched all the videos on the website of other people who had reported that they had recovered from CFS/ME using the Process, and thought that because their symptoms didn't seem as *bad* as hers that the Process probably wouldn't be as helpful for her as it had been for them. Another participant was amazed by this as she had watched exactly the same videos too but because the symptoms of the people in the videos seemed to be *worse* than hers, she suspected that the Process probably wouldn't be as helpful for her as it had been for them.

It seemed that whatever information they were being presented with (sufferers with issues worse than theirs or better than theirs), they somehow managed to use this evidence to help them decide that they would respond *differently*. This meant that whatever evidence they were presented with, even if it documented the success of someone with remarkably similar issues, they would somehow be able to discern a difference between that person's issues and theirs, and therefore eliminate that evidence as having any validity for their case.

Interestingly, in my years of experience of CFS/ME I have never, ever seen any two sufferers with exactly the same set of symptoms and presentation. This is one of the difficulties that both medicine and CFS/ME sufferers have had with this peculiar illness over the years because without consistent findings it's extremely difficult to accurately diagnose.

In the same conversation another participant told how they had heard about our high success rates but had also noted that there were a small percentage of people who didn't get much benefit from undertaking the training. They felt sure that they would be bound, somehow, to be the *same* as the people who didn't benefit from the training.

This tragic combination of excluding yourself (different) from the successful group and aligning yourself (same) with the group who get poor results is something to be avoided at all costs if you want to get maximum value from both the Process and from life itself. I've called this, the 'Same and Different Losing Strategy.'

Talking further we also discovered that in their preparation for the course they had begun to change their perspective and entered into the training with the belief that if it had worked for all those others then it would be bound to work for them (same). If a small proportion of people had used the Process and not got much benefit as a result then they felt sure that they would not be part of that group (different) because they were determined to do the necessary work that the others had done (same). I've called this, the 'Same and Different Success Strategy'.

EXERCISE:
Are you using the 'Same and Different Losing Strategy' or 'Same and Different Success Strategy?'

If you are not using the 'Same and Different Success Strategy', what do you have to do to make sure you are?

Is CFS/ME is easy to recover from?

Most sufferers, carers, support groups and medical opinion think that CFS/ME is an illness that is relatively unresponsive to treatment. Both my experience and that of my ex-CFS/ME clients have found things to be quite different. They report that they have recovered rapidly, in many cases within hours or days of starting to use the Process and stayed well ever since. If you follow the Process, and do what they did, then isn't it reasonable to assume that you should get very similar results too?

EXERCISE:

Do you find this perspective easy to agree with? If yes, you can skip the rest of this exercise. If your answer is no or maybe, then it's vital to answer the following questions. If you are uncertain whether your issues can be resolved easily, considering everything you have read in this book, what do you think the effects of doubting this will be on your ability to makes the changes you want, easily?

1.
2.
3.

What do you need to do, think, or research in order to change this reasonable, but unhelpful belief?

1.
2.
3.

Elements of my findings in CFS/ME cases

For the reasons already discussed I won't be going into huge detail about exactly how the Lightning Process helps people to make profound changes to their health. However, this section has been designed to give you an understanding of some of the elements by giving you a highly edited, simplified and partial version of some of the patterns that I have identified as being core to the maintenance of the complicated symptoms of

CFS/ME. Please keep in mind that this is by no means a complete version, as that is beyond the scope of this book.

One of the patterns I have observed is the disempowering 'treatment response cycle'. This is where:

1. People with CFS/ME are completely committed to finding a cure. They've usually spent thousands of hours researching and thousands of pounds trying treatments to recover.
2. When they discover a new potential route for recovery they begin that new treatment.
3. Very often they will start improving initially, and of course become hopeful that they've finally found the cure.
4. Unfortunately, the initial benefits seem to tail off, they reach a plateau or they start to relapse. The practitioner ups the dose or increases the treatment but it makes less and less difference.
5. Not surprisingly the CFS/ME sufferer gets disappointed again, but because they are committed to finding the cure they start the cycle over but this time with a little less hope and confidence.
6. Each time they go around the cycle, the treatments will often become more extreme, diets will become more restrictive and their condition seems to be more complicated than anyone initially expected.

Now that you have read the section on placebos (page 18 in case you skipped it) you will be much more aware of the affect that these disappointing experiences will have on the effectiveness of treatments as you should now recognise that even the effect of a really strong and powerful drug will be influenced by what we expect is going to happen. As a result, any future treatment (including medical drugs and even surgery) is now bound to be approached with less confidence. This in turn is going to make it less effective.

PER and The Destructive Spiral

This pattern, which has been discussed in chapter 6, helps enormously to support the sufferers' and the medical perspective that CFS/ME is a physical illness and is not all in the mind. Understanding the physiology of the PER and the destructive spiral naturally encourage a holistic perspective as to how the brain and body interact, which in my view, and many other experts in the field, is essential to deal with such a multisystem disease as CFS/ME.

“More than any other issue in contemporary medicine, CFS reflects the unresolved conflict between the mechanistic and biophysical construct of illness.” P Manu in the *American Journal of Medicine* 2000

Leaky Bucket

My experience is that most of the treatments that CFS/ME sufferers have tried in the past have probably been quite good approaches from dedicated and experienced practitioners, and yet the treatment so often fails to make a difference, and frequently any improvements just don’t seem to ‘hold’. The problem is that against this background of internal immune dysfunction, the treatment just hasn’t got a chance of making a big enough difference. It’s like trying to carry water in a leaky bucket; the effects of treatment will just not last. However, once this and the other important elements of the illness are resolved, the body can recover its own equilibrium and begin the process of self-healing.

Your Next Steps

If something in these stories reminds you of your issues then you should ask yourself “If others have made these changes, then why not me?” What do you need to let go of in terms of:

- Your beliefs
- Your ideas
- Things that you think are true about your issues but which might stop you from getting the results you want?
  1.
  2.
  3.
  4.
  5.

When you feel it's time to make these changes and have the life that you would love to have, your next step is to visit the website **www.lightningprocessregister.com** and select a practitioner. Talk to them - they will be very happy to answer any questions you may have. They will guide you through the application process, and if you chose to take a seminar with them, guide you through the Process to discover ways to get a great future.

Chapter 8
Depression

Resolving Depression

Depression is another of those conditions that, for many people, seems to come just by chance and when it's affected them once, it has a tendency to revisit them again and again. Most solutions for depression focus on drug treatments, ways of living with it or long-term deep psychotherapy. However, the Lightning Process has helped many people who suffered with depression to make rapid, lasting and permanent changes, allowing them to free themselves forever from the threat and spectre of this horrible condition.

Emma's Story

Emma had suffered with bad depression on and off since her teens. Learning the Lightning Process was a challenge because the ideas it presented to her and the possibilities that it offered were so different from everything she had ever been told about her depression and her future.

She did recognise though, that the options she had prior to the Lightning Process really weren't working very well for her. Her life was blighted by the depression, which could come at any time and ruin everything for weeks and months. As a result of these failed attempts in the past, she was determined to use the Lightning Process to follow the path that others had to successfully resolve her depression. She says:

> *The Lightning Process was incredible - everything has been going well since. The fact that I could have talked myself completely out of hideous 'depression' in one hour is pretty incontrovertible evidence that it is optional. Something really sunk in and I feel like I'm learning more and more, so thanks very much.*

When I caught up with her a few years later, she reported that her depression was now a thing of the past:

It is astonishing to think how much power it used to have over me and how, before learning the Process, one upsetting event would ruin my life for months afterwards. On the increasingly rare occasions that I ever find myself going down that road to unhappiness I now notice it immediately. Within seconds I am able to steer myself back to happiness with confidence and ease. That feeling of being in charge of the choices in my life is just the best thing ever.

Pete's Story

Pete's story is a particularly interesting one as when he arrived to take the Lightning Process training he was already a fully qualified practitioner of NLP, hypnotherapy and life coaching. Although he had all those skills at his disposal he was unable to shift a deep depression which was, day-by-day, making him more of a recluse, as he had started to avoid going to work or having any social interaction. He says:

I arrived for the Lightning Process feeling absolutely desperate and in a deep depression that had haunted me for years and had been especially bad every day for the last three months.

I had a lack of concentration, was feeling fuzzy, anxious, found it difficult to talk to others, was avoiding my friends and making mistakes at work. Phil trained me in the Lightning Process and, wow, what a difference!

Even after the first session, what a joy to do simple things like read a book, watch TV and actually be present in a conversation again.

It seemed too good to be true but as time has gone on these feelings have continued and strengthened and I am very happy to embrace this new approach. I look forward to getting up in the mornings, the future looks very rosy and it's such a practical process to use in everyday situations that I know I'll stay on track no matter what.

Thanks a bunch Phil!

Pete's Update

Well it is one month now since I came to you to learn the Lightning Process and would like to give you a little update - it is still brilliant! I am so clearly moving more and more into the life I love. Thanks Phil.

Two months later

I thought I would update you on my ongoing Lightning Process experience. I'm going from strength to strength, using the Process less now due to how effective it is being. Things are going well including the schedule of the goals that I set at the clinic. What really stands out is the way I seem to be drawn to situations that I used to avoid. It now seems fun to play with them with the knowledge that I am in control of how I feel!

It's now two years on and Pete reports that he hasn't had a day of depression since attending the Lightning Process.

Your Next Steps

If something in these stories reminds you of your issues then you should ask yourself "If others have made these changes, then why not me?" What do you need to let go of in terms of:

- Your beliefs
- Your ideas
- Things that you think are true about your issues but which might stop you from getting the results you want?
    1.
    2.
    3.
    4.
    5.

When you feel it's time to make these changes and have the life that you would love to have, your next step is to visit the website **www.lightningprocessregister.com** and select a practitioner. Talk to them - they will be very happy to answer any questions you may have. They will guide you through the application process, and if you chose to take a seminar with them, guide you through the Process to discover ways to get a great future.

Chapter 9
Anxiety, Self-esteem, Confidence, Perfectionism and Fear of Failure

Introduction

These issues quite often go hand-in-hand because when you feel anxious all the time you don't feel very good about yourself and you don't feel very competent to go out there and do much for fear of what might happen if you do.

If you don't feel very good about yourself and your abilities, then the world can seem like a very scary place, where things are almost certain to go wrong and it feels like it's due to your inadequacies. As a result, these issues are often linked to those of perfectionism (trying to get everything 100 percent correct all of the time) and fear of failure (which can translate into doing nothing just in case it doesn't turn out perfectly).

Below are a few stories from the thousands that have reported they have recovered from anxiety and other related issues using the Lightning Process.

Anxiety, Panic Attacks and Stress

Anxiety, panic attacks and stress are very unpleasant features of many people's lives. Some common symptoms of anxiety, panic attacks and stress are feeling of being out of control, sweating, having a nervous stomach, the feeling your heart racing, not being able to breathe and constant worrying. These feelings are often overwhelming and horrific.

How common is it?

Anxiety, panic attacks and stress are the emotional states which bring more people into contact with health and business performance clinics than any other. Amazingly, the prevalence of anxiety and depressive disorders in patients who frequently attend general practice is between 40% and 60% (Neal RD, 1998) (Baez K, 1998) (McFarland BH, 1985), so if you suffer with this, you are not alone!

In spite of this however, many people affected by it feel that it carries a social stigma. They are often doing well in their lives, with successful careers when suddenly they are struck down with these worrying stress feelings. This can make them feel as though they are in some way weak, out of control or not able to deal with stress, which unfortunately is itself stressful and undermines their confidence further.

Instead it is more useful to see stress as similar to having a computer virus that has temporarily affected the way your brain's operating system works. Continuing with this metaphor, all you need to get back to being your best is to 'uninstall' that virus, and make sure you are better protected from this kind of viral infection in the future. The Lightning Process is a very effective way to do just that.

April's Story

April had felt bad about herself for most of her life. When she was in her sixties she decided it was time for a change. Below is her assessment of what happened as a result of using the LP.

Before:

> *I would never say what I thought, for fear of upsetting anyone or standing out from the crowd. I felt I had to say 'yes' to everything and everyone. This meant I spent a lot of time doing things I didn't really want to and that I let more vocal friends decide where we went and what we did. This pattern had been part of my life for forty years.*

During:

> *I learnt how to stop putting myself down all the time and how to start to make choices based on what I wanted rather than what I thought other people might want me to do. Since then it's been amazing. I really felt you couldn't 'teach an old dog new tricks' and it was just the way I was but I've seen such a dramatic and positive change in myself over the last few months that I wish I'd known about this earlier. Thanks so much.*

Jan's Story

Every morning I'd wake up feeling dreadful, with my heart racing and thoughts running through my head about everything that was about to go wrong throughout the coming day.

I would constantly be planning how to deal with all the disasters and difficulties that I knew were about to happen, factoring in plans and strategies in case something I hadn't expected also turned up, worrying about the travel arrangements, about the kids, the house and probably all the people of India and few other things besides. I knew I was doing it but I wasn't sure if there was anything I could do to stop it or whether it was just the way I was, because it was something I'd always done.

The morning before I started the Lightning Process I got up at 5.00am to allow myself four hours for the half an hour journey, panicking the whole way through the morning about what might happen and what would go wrong, just as usual. I had to factor in the time to ensure that my hair and make-up were perfect, so I would look okay, although when I left the house I still wasn't happy with how I looked.

By the second day the change was extraordinary. I woke up feeling really relaxed and happy and looking forward to the day. I didn't worry about my hair, took a leisurely breakfast, did some stuff I'd been putting off for ages and took it easy. When I got off the bus at the wrong stop, instead of getting stressed, I just worked out how to get to the seminar, calmly, by using the Process. Life just became much more simple, easy and fun.

But this was just the beginning of a transformation in my life and my future. Since then the anxiety, that had been with me all the time for years and years, just isn't there anymore. I look forward to each day, taking things as they come, dealing with things that I need to deal with and having more fun than I could ever imagine.

Susan's Story

Susan was ten and had been suffering from low self-esteem, failing confidence at school, poor school work and a diagnosis of borderline dyspraxia. Her story is quite typical of the feedback we get when working with these kinds of problems. After taking the Lightning Process, both Susan and her mum sent us this report:

My ten year old daughter had been suffering from worry and anxiety for two years. Her confidence and self-esteem were low, and small things would set-off the cycle of worry. This affected everyday life and she would have three to four 'worries' a day. For example she would worry that the cat might run away or that I might crash the car. Nothing I said or did made any difference. School work suffered and life was very strained for both of us. She constantly worked herself up into hysterical frenzies.

Someone recommended the LP to us, saying what a difference it had made in their life. Naturally I was apprehensive at first, it sounded too good to be true and even a tad 'wacky' but on meeting Phil I was pleasantly surprised. He was laid back and brilliant with Susan. He knew how to put her at ease and after the Lightning Process sessions he had taught her how to stop anxieties and worrying. She seems happier now and puts things in perspective. The change in my daughter is unbelievable and her recent school grade card was the best ever. Straight As and 1s.

I'd recommend Phil and the Lightning Process to anyone having difficulties in their life.

Susan wrote:

I heard about Phil through a friend, who'd told me he was very good so my mum decided to take me to see him. When I first got there I felt very nervous and was worried about what was going to happen. While we were waiting I began to shake and get sweaty palms but when I got in the room and we had the first session it was really good.

At the end of the week I sat down and talked with my mum about what I had worried about over the week. We realised that I had only worried twice the whole week, which was a big difference.

May's Story

May is eight and had been suffering from anxiety attacks for some years. Again her story is quite typical of the feedback we get when working with these kinds of problems:

To Phil, thank you for making me feel better and I appreciate it very, very, very, very, very, very much.

Before I went to Phil I felt very nervous about going to school, going to parties, staying at family and friend's houses, learning the flute and anything else I could worry about. This made me feel sad and miserable and I thought these feelings would never end. I was very worried about seeing Phil and I was shaking but he wasn't scary and he treated me nicely. Since I've seen Phil and learnt the Lightning Process I know how to deal with myself when I get nervous and worried. Also I have felt very happy and jolly. Thank you Phil.

Her mum adds:

I decided to take my daughter May to see Phil because her confidence and happiness was deteriorating and nothing I did or said helped anymore. As a caring mother I felt helpless and so wanted May to be her happy self again. May would cry a lot, she didn't want to leave me, or go to school, parties, or stay with friends or family, the list was endless. We couldn't see any problems at school or home, you know bullying etc. Then a friend recommended Phil, so I made an appointment and he was so good with May, so reassuring.

The three day seminar she had with Phil made such a fantastic difference. She became much happier, more confident and enjoyed life and being a child again. Even her teacher came to tell me how happy she is in class. My husband and I wish to say many thanks to you, Phil.

A Doctor's Story: Confidence

When she came to see me she was very nervous. It wasn't the sort of thing she would normally do; after all she was a doctor.

She had been progressing very well in her medical career, excelling in the A and E department of a London teaching hospital but the time had come when she needed to make the decision to become a fellow of the Royal College of Physicians. This involved some very difficult practical exams and the success rates of passing were not very high. There were also only a limited number of chances to take the exam - when you had used your chances that was it.

Despite being brilliant, having extensive experience of working with real patients and having an in-depth knowledge of her subject, she went to pieces when it came to the exams. It didn't help that she was a woman and the majority of examiners were male, that she was also much smaller than them and had quite different values and beliefs systems than they did. The whole exam environment felt completely alien to her. When she came to see me she had almost run out of chances and was about to take her final exam. If she failed this time then she would never become a fellow of the college.

However, within a day of starting the Lightning Process, everything changed. Her confidence improved beyond anything she could have imagined and she felt sure she would be able to be her best both at work in the A and E department as well as in the difficult clinical exams. She knew that if the examiners tried to intimidate her, as they had seemed to do in the past, she could deal with that too.

A few weeks later she rang me to let me know how she'd got on. She didn't have the results in yet but she was pretty confident that she had done excellently, as she had easily dealt with all the things that previously would have made her go to pieces. When the results came out she had passed the exam with flying colours.

This is an excellent example of one of the common ironies of life. It seems in certain situations and times we show ourselves to be someone who has all the ability, knowledge and confidence we need to make the best of things. Yet in other situations and times we seem unable to get in touch with those abilities and confidence at the very time when we really need them. One of the things the Lightning Process taught her, and could teach you, is how to get in touch with those talents and abilities, at will and anytime you need to. If you could master just this skill, how would that change your future?

Your Next Steps

If something in these stories reminds you of your issues then you should ask yourself "If others have made these changes, then why not me?" What do you need to let go of in terms of:

- Your beliefs
- Your ideas
- Things that you think are true about your issues but which might stop you from getting the results you want?
  1.
  2.
  3.
  4.
  5.

When you feel it's time to make these changes and have the life that you would love to have, your next step is to visit the website **www.lightningprocessregister.com** and select a practitioner. Talk to them - they will be very happy to answer any questions you may have. They will guide you through the application process, and if you chose to take a seminar with them, guide you through the Process to discover ways to get a great future.

Chapter 10
Weight and Eating Issues

Introduction

Everyone knows that the solution to becoming the appropriate weight is to eat and exercise the right amounts. However, there is only one X factor, which is to make sure that you do this *consistently*. The Lightning Process is an extremely effective method for helping you to learn how to be consistent in doing these relatively simple things and as a result will help you to achieve your goal of having a good, healthy and appropriate weight.

It's also been very valuable in helping people with even more complex food related issues including eating disorders such as anorexia and bulimia. As with many issues such as these it can be easy to find yourself overwhelmed by the sheer scale of the problem you are facing and resigned to change being impossible or difficult. However the first step to finding a solution is remember that in spite of how often you've been told that change is unlikely or hard to achieve, if others have achieved what you want, then it must be possible to get what you want too.

Jill's Story

Up to three months ago, I had a problem around food. As a child I refused to eat as much food as I needed. I have many memories of the battles I had around food and not wanting to eat. Between the ages of eleven to thirteen, this changed to binge eating and periods of not eating at all. I hid this well from my family and didn't take it to the extreme of putting my life in danger, but it did have a great affect on my life and how I felt about myself. I booked a place on the Lightning Process with Phil to make the changes I wanted to make. I noticed a profound change after the first day, I no longer felt driven to binge. I used the Process to deal with the underlying reasons why I did this and I now have a healthy relationship with food - something that I had not experienced before.

Spurred on by this, I decided to work through an underlying belief that I was inferior to others. This manifested itself as being an extremely shy child and feeling driven to please others to the detriment of myself. The changes I've achieved using the Process have been immense, simple to achieve and magical.

Camilla's Story

For years I'd battled with my weight, self-image and food. Binge eating, followed by vomiting and guilt were my daily experiences. That was until I came across the Lightning Process. Amazingly in just a few hours it all changed. I wasn't sure it would last. Well you just don't, after so long - do you? After six months, I was at last eating sensibly, feeling good about myself and not vomiting. Suddenly a tiny event brought home exactly how much I had changed.

It was Christmas time and the office that I worked in had a huge bowl of sweets for everyone to tuck into. Usually I'd grab handfuls when no one was looking. This year I was able to walk past it without even a second thought - amazing. Thanks Phil for teaching me what I was missing in my life.

Your Next Steps

If something in these stories reminds you of your issues then you should ask yourself, "If others have made these changes, then why not me?" What do you need to let go of in terms of:

- Your beliefs
- Your ideas
- Things that you think are true about your issues but which might stop you from getting the results you want?
    1.
    2.
    3.

4.
5.

When you feel it's time to make these changes and have the life that you would love to have, your next step is to visit the website **www.lightningprocessregister.com** and select a practitioner. Talk to them - they will be very happy to answer any questions you may have. They will guide you through the application process, and if you chose to take a seminar with them, guide you through the Process to discover ways to get a great future.

Chapter 11
Obsessive Compulsive Disorder (OCD)

This debilitating condition severely limits many people's lives; most approaches consider there is no cure for it, and that sufferers should resign themselves to finding ways to best manage the effects that it has on their lives.

Keith's story

Keith was one such sufferer, who discovered there is a simple way out, the Lightning Process. He had many repetitive behaviours such as checking whether the cooker really was off (often twelve times or more) before he left his house. These checking rituals had been more and more frequent and his self-confidence was daily being battered by his inability to be, as he put it 'just normal'.

> *I have been an OCD sufferer for as many years as I can remember. On many occasions it would consume me to such a degree that I would not want to go out or drive to a destination that I had never been to before. I had tried many different counsellors and doctors, all without success but then my niece saw Phil and recovered from CFS/ME after having it for two years. I decided to give it a go.*
>
> *Well, the results have been fantastic! By using the Lightning Process I have been able to reduce my OCD by 75 percent at least, and will have it licked the more I use the Process. I am now more confident, happier and have more energy. I can only say a big 'thank you' to Phil, for helping me overcome something that was controlling my life.*

Keith updated us one month later:

> *The OCD is now almost a thing of the past. I recently went to New York for the weekend and was able to pack my bags in a flash (it used to take me hours of worrying if I'd taken enough of the right kinds of*

> *clothes). I was even able to take just a small bag rather than my usual huge suitcase. I only checked the house was locked up once (like a normal person) before leaving and then had a brilliant time whilst away. Even when an old habitual ritual raises its head, which is now hardly ever, I now know how to stop it in its tracks which feels great!*

One of the core patterns in OCD is a 'checking pattern'. This is where someone checks repeatedly in case they have missed that 'important something' (germs, turning off the cooker, etc.) and imagines exactly how bad the consequences would be of forgetting to do something and how repeatedly checking to do it, they've kept themselves and others 'safe' so far.

The OCD Loop

A rather unpleasant 'circular argument' is found in almost all cases. It relies on the evidence they have collected over the years about keeping themselves and others safe by continuing the rituals, and focuses on the times when they failed to do that ritual and something bad did happen. It runs something like this:

1. So far they've avoided the disaster they've been expecting.
2. This has been achieved because they've done their OCD habits.
3. To avoid these potential disasters occurring in the future they need to continue protecting themselves and loved ones by continuing their OCD behaviours.
4. On the few occasions they didn't perform their OCD behaviour, something bad did happen, which confirms the truth of steps 1 and 2.
5. To do anything else would be foolish and dangerous.

Some of this information has been identified in the past by others but what's new in the Lightning Process is a description and set of instructions detailing how to break out of the destructive cycle and how to change this behaviour.

Your Next Steps

If something in this story reminds you of your issues then you should ask yourself "If others have made these changes, then why not me?" What do you need to let go of in terms of:

- Your beliefs
- Your ideas
- Things that you think are true about your issues but which might stop you from getting the results you want?
    1.
    2.
    3.
    4.
    5.

When you feel it's time to make these changes and have the life that you would love to have, your next step is to visit the website **www.lightningprocessregister.com** and to select a practitioner. Talk to them - they will be very happy to answer any questions you may have. They will guide you through the application process, and if you chose to take a seminar with them, guide you through the Process to discover ways to get a great future.

Chapter 12
Multiple Sclerosis (MS)

MS is a chronic condition that affects the central nervous system. The actual cause of Multiple Sclerosis (MS) is relatively unknown. Symptoms vary and not everyone with MS will suffer from all symptoms.

Some of the most common are:

- Dizziness and balance difficulties
- Numbness and tingling
- Fatigue
- Cognitive problems
- Muscle spasms
- Mood changes

There are three 'types' of MS - Relapsing Remitting MS, Secondary Progressive MS and Primary Progressive MS.

Rather excitingly we have seen a number of people with all the different types of MS reporting impressive results when using the LP.

Why LP might be considered as an option for MS?

There are some interesting factors in the natural history of the MS illness which first made me consider it as a potential issue that might respond well to the LP:

- MS is characterised by the presence of plaques or sclerotic lesions, which appear on the myelin sheaths of the nerves. They are considered to be the cause of reduced nerve function in MS and the key diagnostic factor of MS. When people with the relapsing remitting type of MS (which means the symptoms fluctuated in intensity - sometimes disappearing all together) were examined the findings were surprising. The lesions seemed to be relatively unchanged during both the good and bad phases of the illness.

- This suggests that the lesions themselves can't be the only factors involved in the expression of the disease and that that there must be some other variables at work that mediate the strength of the symptoms. The question I asked was, "Is it possible to affect any of these other factors using the LP?" One of these suggested factors that may influence the intensity of symptoms is called the Physical Emergency Response (PER), which is we have covered in chapter 6. Learning to affect this response is one of the goals of the LP training.
- There is debate as to whether MS is a neurological or immunological condition, but as the LP has already had good results with illnesses caused by dysfunctions in both these systems, this seems to be a good indicator that there is a possibility of making changes with MS too.

With these thoughts in mind we began to work with people with MS to see what kind of results could be achieved. Some of these people's stories follow.

MS Case Report 1

This was sent in from a 61 year old lady who was diagnosed with progressive MS seven years before she took the LP, although she had been having symptoms for about six years before that. Her symptoms include fatigue and muscle weakness along with bladder and bowel problems. She was limited to walking about 100 yards without a cane, and was unable to stand unaided, or walk on gravel or up/down slopes.

After the first day she found she was able to walk 200 yards, and by day two could walk unaided for 30 minutes, and was noticing improvement in her bladder control

A week later she reported she had walked 600 yards to the postbox, up a slope and over gravel the first time in four years. She stated that she had walked and stood still chatting to friends for one hour, that she had played 27 holes of golf (using a buggy between holes) and walked along the seafront.

Four weeks later she reported that she had done a 1.6 mile walk unaided.

Sixteen months later she reported that she has no MS symptoms for 99.9% of the time and if she feels her feet are a little stiff, she will use the LP to get improvements. She reports that she can walk a full round of golf anytime she wants to, on consecutive days if desired, go out and socialise, travel on long haul flights, help others who are in need and still have good energy and ability to live life to the full with friends and family.

MS Case Report 2

This was sent in by a 61 year old man who was diagnosed with progressive MS about five years before taking the LP, although he reported that his symptoms started 15 years before that.

His symptoms included being unable to stand or weight bear for the past five years, combined with muscle pain, weakness and loss of sensation in his legs, some loss of bladder control, intermittent 'nerve pain and a pulling sensation' and some problems with his vision.

After day one he reported that he was able to walk for 100 yards with crutches which was much further than before.

By day three he reported that his muscle pain and weakness were mostly gone and that he was able to weight bear with minimal support.

A week later he had clipped his hedge, been out socialising, and was walking further distances without a stick, and even showered himself for the first time in years. He also reported that his bladder control was normal and that his vision had improved slightly.

Twelve weeks later he reported he was able to bend, balance and play bowls; including walk the distances between ends, up to 24 times; he can do six squats each morning and the nerve pain and pulling sensation has completely gone.

Four months later he stated that he could carry logs into the house using both hands without a stick over rough ground for 200 yards.

At six months he stated that his legs were stronger and that he could lift them higher and quicker. He reported that his symptoms had generally held or improved slightly again.

Your Next Steps

If something in this story reminds you of your issues then you should ask yourself "If others have made these changes, then why not me?" What do you need to let go of in terms of:

- Your beliefs
- Your ideas
- Things that you think are true about your issues but which might stop you from getting the results you want?
  1.
  2.
  3.
  4.
  5.

When you feel it's time to make these changes and have the life that you would love to have, your next step is to visit the website **www.lightningprocessregister.com** and select a practitioner. Talk to them - they will be very happy to answer any questions you may have. They will guide you through the application process, and if you chose to take a seminar with them, guide you through the Process to discover ways to get a great future.

Chapter 13
Physiology

Introduction

I've included an additional section on some of the physiology and neuroscience that has been instrumental in the development of the Lightning Process. I'd recommend that you read it, even if you have an aversion to science, as it's written for the layman and we've found that a deeper understanding of the science behind the Process can be very valuable.

Neuroplasticity

One of the core concepts of the Lightning Process is to utilize the ability of the brain and body to influence each other and to train participants to use this influence in a healthy, life enhancing way. Much scientific research has already been done by others (Edelman, Kandel etc.) into how the brain learns, some of this research gives us a useful insight into why the Lightning Process works so rapidly and effectively.

How the Brain Learns

In neuroscience the brain is considered to be 'plastic', which means it has the ability to grow and develop in response to how it is used. So the more you stimulate a particular neural pathway the better it works and the quicker a signal travels down that pathway. It's like the difference between dial-up and broadband internet or between a country track and multi-lane motorway. Look at the following picture to see how the pathways in the brain work.

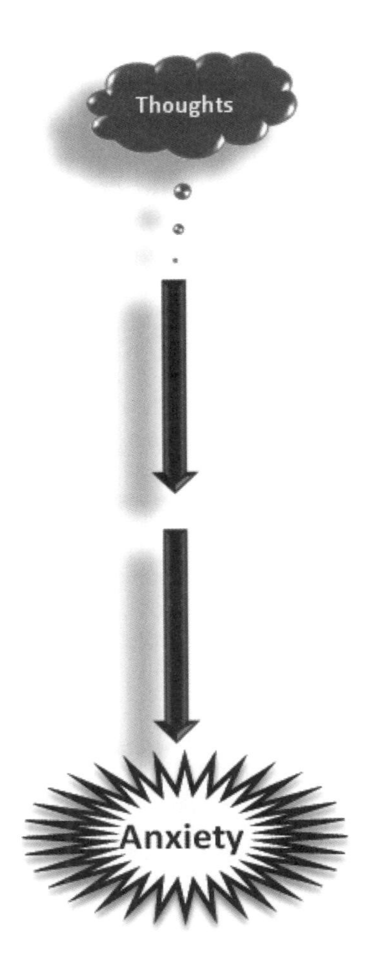

The thoughts create a signal that is transmitted along the nerve cells in the direction of the arrow. Once the signal has travelled all the way to the end of this particular pathway it will create (in this example) the feelings and experience of anxiety.

In the following diagram, additional thoughts have started to trigger that anxiety. This extra usage results in a 'strengthening' and increase in speed of this pathway and therefore, it becomes easier and easier to produce the feelings of anxiety each time.

If you are someone who is used to anxiety in your life then the pathway that's responsible for the feelings of anxiety will be very well developed and fast and it will also have lots of connections to other parts of the brain. The more connections a pathway has and the more it's used and triggered, the faster it will become. In the same way as a fast motorway with good links to lots of destinations will be used more than one that goes to less places.

This means that even the least consequential events can activate that pathway. For example, when someone with a highly developed anxiety pathway sees someone who looks very calm, it may remind them of how they hardly ever feel calm and that will be enough to instantly trigger their anxiety pathway and give them feelings of anxiety.

They may see a soap opera on TV and because one of the characters in it is worrying about their daughter, it may trigger their own anxiety about their child.

They may see a person in a shop that reminds them of a mean teacher they used to know and that may trigger their anxiety.

In this way many things start to connect to and fire off this anxiety pathway and because the brain grows in response to how much it is used this pathway becomes very, very fast. It becomes like a super-highway in your nervous system and it runs very quickly and very effectively. This is how powerful feelings of anxiety can be produced with the slightest trigger.

Consider another example. Imagine a woman who had just had a miscarriage and lost her baby. The next time she went into town what would she see everywhere?

Babies.

And what shops would she notice?

Baby shops.

And if there weren't any baby shops in that part of town what would she notice about her shopping experience?

That there weren't any baby shops.

If she saw people who were about sixty years old on her trip how would that remind her of her loss?

That they used to be babies or that they have grandchildren.

In this scenario the recently developed pathway related to the miscarriage is taking her into a deep sense of loss, but unfortunately the brain is making millions of connections from all sorts of random bits of information, like the 'people who are about sixty years old', directly into the loss pathway, so it gets triggered all the time. This exercising of that particular set of nerve pathways in the brain makes them much easier to activate (technically the synaptic threshold is decreased, the spark jumps the gap between nerve cells easier and they become what's called 'facilitated') and the 'thoughts' travel quicker and more frequently down that pathway triggered by the bad feelings.

This may make you think that if you've got such a well rehearsed neurological pathway that produces intense negative feelings in your brain in response to even the slightest thing, then the situation is hopeless. Far from it. This ability of the brain to learn is key to your route to success.

When people learn to apply the Lightning Process they begin to divert the way that pathway works. Each time they do this they will be creating a new connection within the nervous tissue of the brain so that as soon as those old pathways are triggered they now activate a completely new, completely different pathway.

This pathway begins by being triggered by the same events as before but now it leads them into making better choices rather than just ending in the neurological cul-de-sac of an unpleasant set of feelings or a bad state.

If you're one of our readers who left school some time ago, there are probably all sorts of subjects that you learnt such as long division, algebra or maybe a foreign language such as French or German, which you haven't used much since those school days. When you are suddenly presented with an opportunity to use those long forgotten skills, what happens? Your brain rustily tries to remember the dimly recalled formula for how to do these things or the words that you once learnt long ago for 'punctured tyre' or 'run out of petrol' in French.

You find yourself really grappling with your brain to try and find this information, but it's not that easy to access now as this is a pathway that you haven't used for a long time and because the brain is 'plastic', when you don't use pathways, they degrade and slow down.

In the old days, in England, there used to be very important roads that people used to drive their cattle to market and these roads were well used and well maintained. With the advent of trucks and railways, people didn't drive their cattle to market anymore and they didn't herd their cattle along these paths. They took them in trucks and trains and the pathways became overgrown with weeds and the surfaces got washed away by the rain and now even if you look really hard you can barely find them.

This is exactly what starts to happen in your brain as you apply the Lightning Process. The first steps of those old pathways that used to produce the negative feelings or un-useful behaviours or physiological responses in your life are still being triggered as always but they are now quickly re-routed to new areas of the brain that can produce better responses for you. The old parts of the pathway, the bits that actually produced the negative feelings, don't get used in this new pathway and so start to slow down and degrade. Even if those pathways have been very well established, research into brain function and learning suggests that they can change quite rapidly. There are two main reasons why this is quite rapid:

- The brain naturally learns quickly
  You can test the truth of this quite easily. Consider your postcode or zip code. What are the first three parts of it, including the letters and numbers? Now, without writing it down, say the sequence of letters and numbers

backwards. This is a piece of information that you've probably never had to use before, so it's creating a new pathway in your brain. Although this might be quite tricky at first, after just a few rehearsals you can say this sequence forwards or backwards quite easily because our brain learns fast.

- Thousands of opportunities
  When you use the Lightning Process, you will have a great deal of opportunity to re-pattern your brain.

  This is why it's so essential to use the Lightning Process appropriately, remembering that it is not a therapy or treatment but a re-education, a learning process that occurs not just during the seminar but afterwards. If you learn it but only apply it occasionally or for a brief period, the results won't be that good, as you will either have not retrained your brain enough for it to be used in the new way of operating or you will be once again re-energising the old unhealthy pathways that you actually need to sedate.

For the majority of the small group of people who get few or variable results from learning the Process, this is what is missing in their application of the Process. If, having read the book, you choose to learn the Process, please keep in mind that you need to give your brain a chance to establish the new patterns and let the old ones fade away. This is essential if you wish to replicate the success of others, after all, that's what they had to do to get the results that they got.

Background Neurology

A little understanding of what's going on inside your body can be useful to make sense of the sometimes challenging concepts presented in this book. This section is provided to give some more background to the PER and destructive spiral information in chapter 6. Please note that this is only a brief description of the complex systems involved, if you want more details on this research there are many books you can read on the subject, and this is covered in more depth in the Lightning Process seminars.

The Sympathetic Nervous System

The nervous system is divided up in the following way:

1. The voluntary nervous system, which is the bit that we control directly. When we want to move our arm to reach an object, we are in direct control of that movement.
2. The involuntary (or autonomic) nervous system is the bit that we don't normally control directly. This includes functions like the movement of our digestive system, the speed of our heartbeat, the tension in the walls of our blood vessels which affects our blood pressure, the amount we sweat, etc. This part of the nervous system has two further divisions. The sympathetic nervous system (SNS) and the parasympathetic nervous system (PNS).

The easiest way to think of these is to consider thousands of years ago, when we lived close to dangerous wild animals. Imagine a tiger appears. We need to either:

- Run very fast
- Fight it with all our might

Both these actions are prepared for by the activation of the PER which is designed to deal with threats. It prepares us for flight or fight and allows the body to channel all its energy into the muscles of our arms and legs, for our heart to beat faster and stronger, for the blood to be pumped more quickly through our body (by increasing our blood pressure) and for us to have lots of blood sugar available to be burnt by our muscles as fuel. These changes are all controlled by the SNS.

There is much less of a need, in this crisis moment, to do cave painting, digest, cook food or even heal yourself (these activities are all controlled by the PNS). These things would waste precious energy and resources that need to be totally available for the vital job of escaping or beating the danger. A few minutes later one of the following things will have happened:

- You will have killed the tiger
- You will have escaped from the tiger
- You will have been eaten by the tiger

If either one or two above has occurred then the danger has now passed and you can begin to calm down, tend to your wounds, nurture yourself and recover from your experience. This means that you can switch off the PER quieten down the SNS and let the PNS takes over.

This way of operating causes modern day man a problem. Unfortunately most of the threats we encounter are not like tigers. They don't come along, require physical activity from us and then get resolved in this relatively rapid way. Many tend to be things that would be completely inappropriate to respond physically to (by fighting or running away) such as mortgages, waiting in queues, dealing with bosses or customers etc.

They tend to be things that don't resolve rapidly, i.e. bosses don't just go away, mortgages have to be paid every month for twenty plus years etc. We respond in this way because that's how we are designed to respond.

One of the key questions for us today is, if that's just the way our bodies work then we have to find a way of responding to these events in a different way if we want to survive and flourish in the 21st century.

Chapter 14
Useful Information and Research

Register of Lightning Process Practitioners

The Register has been created to ensure that when you take the Lightning Process your practitioner has been extensively trained by Phil Parker and passed the necessary assessments to be qualified to deliver the training.

In order to be granted a licence to practice and to be accepted onto the Register practitioners are required to maintain their Continuing Professional Development (CPD), undertake supervision and agree to abide by the Code of Ethics and Professional Conduct.

As with any field there is always a tendency for a small number of unqualified people to claim that they have skills which they don't or credentials that they are not entitled to, so for your safety please ensure that your practitioner is properly qualified and registered by checking their details on the register which is available online at **www.lightningprocessregister.com**

Please note that there is only one Register. If anyone suggests that they can train you in the Lightning Process, or something like or derived from it and they are not on the Register then they are not licensed to use the Lightning Process and will not be current with its latest research and developments.

Format of Delivery

When training someone to use the Lightning Process to change their life or health we have found it works best to follow this schedule:

- The course takes place in small groups or as one-to-one sessions and is carried out over three consecutive days each lasting approximately 3-5 hours.
- A one-to-one follow-up consultation is strongly advised about a week after your training to ensure you are on track

and to answer any questions that may have arisen. These are usually between twenty to thirty minutes by phone. Face-to-face appointments are also available if required, as is additional support.

- After the seminar has finished you are advised to stay in touch with your practitioner as much as you need. Your practitioner is there for you if you just have a question or if you feel you need some further support. Some people find they have all the tools they need after the three days and rarely contact their practitioner, except to keep them updated with the exciting changes they are making in their lives.

- Building Your Future seminars have been developed to provide on-going support. The seminars are designed to re-cover the core points of the training programme and assist you in moving forwards with any old or new issues and challenges that might arise.

Is it available over the phone or internet?

We have in the past attempted to teach the Process by these methods but have not found them very effective. As a result we no longer teach the Process other than in face-to-face seminars because we want to ensure that you get the best chance of making a difference in your life and health by having the seminar delivered properly and effectively.

Where is it available?

As I write this, the Lightning Process is currently available across many countries in Europe including the United Kingdom and Scandinavia. It is also available in North America and Australasia. However, as the success of the LP spreads we will be taking it to new countries; so if your country is not yet listed here, please get in touch with us to discuss training options.

For the most up to date information about where the LP is currently available please visit our website **www.lightningprocessregister.com**

Practitioner Training

What training and qualifications does a Lightning Process practitioner have? Not everyone can be a Lightning Process Practitioner as it takes quite a special type of person to lead you through what may well be the most important, and occasionally challenging, experience of your life. They need to be trained to a very high level in NLP, Coaching and Clinical Hypnotherapy and they need to be familiar with huge amounts of physiology and have a deep understanding of how the brain and body interact.

They need to have completed a very stretching, in-depth year long training and to have demonstrated their effectiveness to an expert in the field in a clinical exam. Above all, they need to be astute practitioners who are able to be compassionate and caring whilst ensuring that you are addressing the issues that you need to, especially the ones that you might normally avoid dealing with.

Research

We are keen to undertake research in a number of areas. Whilst there are many anecdotal accounts of people who report improvement after attending Lightning Process seminars we recognise that we need to establish an evidence base from research projects to provide scientific substantiation. Some of the research studies are mentioned here to give you an idea of the range of possibilities for the Lightning Process.

We currently have two randomised controlled trials (RCTs) in the design stages. We are also currently involved in a feasibility study with the NHS to look at if we can recruit young people into a study.

We feel that a formally conducted study is the best way to ensure that the results we have through the anecdotal evidence can be replicated under research conditions to demonstrate the efficacy of the Lightning Process. It is essential that the studies include calculation of strength, diagnostic inclusion criterion, standardised intervention, relevant control group, validated and relevant outcome measures, follow-up, and correct statistics. It is also essential that this research is published in well-reputed peer-reviewed journals to ensure validity of the research techniques and their findings.

More details will be released once the findings are collated and some conclusions are drawn, as that will be the most appropriate time to discuss the impact of the research. We will keep the website (**www.lightningprocess.com/Research/**) up-to-date with any details that can be released.

Another project is looking at the effects of the Lightning Process for those with MS in a Proof of Concept study. A small number of volunteers are completing questionnaires before and after attending an LP course, which will then be analysed and results published on our website. We need much more data before we can make any firm claims of beneficial effects. We are currently looking for research partners from the medical and academic professions in order to take this work forward.

Lightning Process Practitioners also conduct snapshot surveys in order to gain feedback on the effectiveness of the training that they have delivered and what changes the client has experienced by day three of the course. We are currently reviewing methods of following these up at intervals in the future to determine the success of using the Lightning Process over time.

We are also due to start a data collection exercise where Lightning Process Practitioners will ask their clients to complete standardised outcome measures in order to track changes clients report following their attendance at an LP seminar.

We are collating a database of conditions that Lightning Process Practitioners have worked with and are building up our anecdotal evidence base with case studies contributed by practitioners.

How the training is conducted?

Much will be demanded from you over the three days of the seminar, but if you take on the challenge, the rewards are extraordinary. Your practitioner has a very demanding role during the seminars. They not only have to present the material but also manage and assist you as you go through this very challenging process. There are certain ground rules that will make the training easier for you and them.

Your trainer is completely committed to your success and as a result will work hard on your behalf with care and integrity.

Your role in the training

The LP is all about you and your future; and as it is your future, you will have the biggest role in the LP seminar, and will have to do the most work, and be very determined. This is why we recommend that you have more of a commitment to the training and your success than just 'wanting to give it a go'.

You will need to:

- Be ready to make changes
- Be open to feedback
- Be ready to examine your beliefs

Working together with your practitioner in this way provides the easiest route to powerful positive change.

Next Step

If, after reading this book, visiting the website and talking to a practitioner, you have decided to apply for the training, then you will need to complete an application form. This is available from your chosen practitioner.

Once they have received your application, your practitioner will contact you to discuss the course and your application with you. Reading this book should have prepared you well for your discussion with them.

Chapter 15
Pre-course Preparation

Once you've sent off your application form you will have a pre-course discussion with your practitioner. This is to answer any questions you may have and prepare you to get the most from the course. It is possible that your practitioner might suggest some homework for you to complete before starting the course.

Congruency of Beliefs

Throughout the book we have recognised how influential beliefs are in everything that we do, this will of course include your health and the LP training. It's important therefore, to consider beliefs in more detail, particularly how they were formed, what they are currently and how we can begin to change the ones that aren't very useful to us anymore.

How beliefs are formed

Wherever something is taken as read, assumed to be true, common knowledge or generalised, we have a belief in operation. Beliefs are generated in a time when we discover a gap in our understanding. The process of their creation goes something like this:

- At some point in our past we came across something new and unexpected.
- We didn't understand it.
- This left us feeling confused and paralysed by that sense of 'just not understanding'.
- We needed to make sense of it.
- We created a belief that bridged the gap in our knowledge.
- This allowed us a way of understanding things so that at least we could continue to function rather than be paralysed by 'just not knowing'.
- We survived.
- We recognised we had survived.

- We applied the same belief to combat other similar situations and found this allowed us to 'know' what to do/think/how to react in those situations.
- This happened a few times.
- We stored this belief as a reliable fact.
- We used it so often we mistook it for the truth, for reality, rather than a useful approximation of what worked for us in those kinds of situations.

A simple example is learning how to open doors. Doors are a mystery to children at first. They seem to be walls sometimes and openings at other times. They don't understand them. Then, one wonderful day, usually at about fourteen months old, they work out that adults get through walls by pushing or pulling the 'door' to open it. Armed with this knowledge, they now understand the magic of doors and can apply it in every room in their house and in all other buildings too. It serves them very well.

Until they meet that strangest of things - the sliding door. When an adult finds themselves, unknowingly, at a sliding door, what do they do? First they push it, then pull it, then they do the same again but harder. Then they kick it, they think it's locked or stuck and then finally by chance they might notice it doesn't have hinges, or feel the sideways motion of it and only then do they realise that the old technology based on their well established belief about opening doors is inappropriate here. Beliefs are special kinds of generalisations in that they are often so fundamentally believed and unquestioned that we forget they are there, even though they affect our thinking in all situations.

The Language of Beliefs

They are usually expressed as statements of fact, and often include:

- All, every, ever, never etc. (technically called *universal quantifiers*)

- I can, you can't etc. (technically called *modal operators of possibility*)
- I must, I must not etc. (technically called *modal operators of necessity*)
- I am, they are, it is - type phrases

For example:

- "I am no good." Notice that this statement is not limited to "I am no good *today*" and really means "I am *never* any good".
- "*All* rich people are mean."
- "You *can't* cure anorexia."
- "I *mustn't* upset others."

Beliefs do not respond to logical intervention. For example, it is very difficult to argue or reason someone out of 'hating themselves' to 'liking themselves'. Most racists know someone who belongs to the racial group they despise and yet they think that individual is 'not bad'. For example, an Anglophobe hates English people, but may consider Isaac Newton to be 'not a bad man', but this doesn't stop them knowing 'the English are all useless'.

It is completely possible to hold two or more conflicting beliefs at the same time. In English football, one team's fans may hate another team's fans and yet, during the World Cup, when England's national team play Germany's some of the fans will all join together in hating Germany's fans. Or they may support Germany if they are playing Argentina (for those who don't know, there is still some animosity in certain sections of English society towards both the Germans and the Argentineans since fighting them some considerable time ago in the World Wars and the Falklands War).

The Sixth Commandment "Thou shalt not kill" is still held by the chaplains who bless the troops before they go into battle. It is not unusual to have a mixture of opposing beliefs but it does tend to make things more complicated for us. Success is most easily achieved in any field of endeavour when our beliefs are aligned.

Beliefs Exercise

Robert Dilts, one of the foremost NLP authors and researchers, has spent some time looking at the power and influence that beliefs have on all aspects of human endeavour and especially the influence that they have on our health. The following exercise is adapted from his important work in this field.

Use the following format to help you identify what your beliefs are about 'resolving your issues'.

Score yourself on a scale of one to five, where one means you disagree strongly with the statement and five means you completely agree with the statement. The answers to these questions may seem so obvious that quite often people are surprised to notice that their actual beliefs don't quite match what they thought they would be and what they thought they should be.

Statement one: I want to resolve all of my issues.

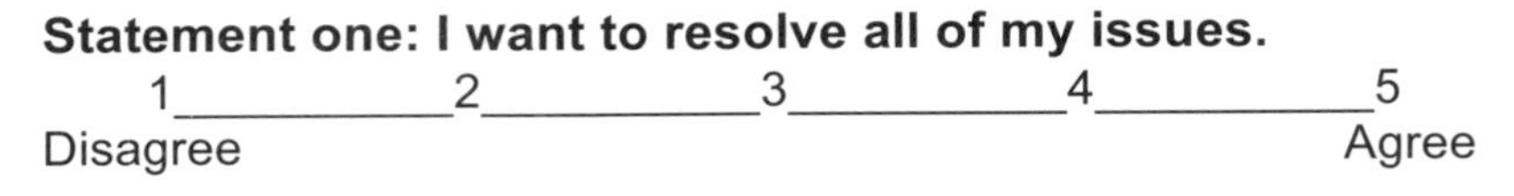

If your score here is less than five then you need to get more clarity about whether you want this change. The other questions will help you identify why your score is less than five.

Statement two: It is possible for me to resolve all of my issues.

1__________2__________3__________4__________5
Disagree Agree

It's important to distinguish this question from the next one. This question is really about whether it is possible or impossible to resolve the issues. You want to consider this question a bit like being alive or dead or being pregnant or not pregnant, in that you can't really be halfway between.

Similarly, if something is not impossible, then by definition, it must be possible.

Statement three: I am capable of resolving all of my issues.

1__________2__________3__________4__________5
Disagree Agree

This question is considering whether or not you have the capabilities to make the changes you wish for. It is a bit like assembling a piece of flat packed furniture or making a jigsaw puzzle. If, when you take it out of the box, you find there are pieces missing then you do not currently have the capability to assemble the furniture or complete the jigsaw. Without the correct components it is just simply beyond your capabilities.

If your issues are about health, for example, do you have the correct components for healing? They would include your immune system, blood, oxygen, etc. For the moment let us ignore the fact that you will also need some knowledge of how to get these systems working properly, as this is something that will be covered in the seminars.

Statement four: It is appropriate and good for me and my life for me to resolve all of my issues and I am prepared to do what it takes to make the changes.

1__________2__________3__________4__________5
Disagree Agree

This is asking if there would there be any negative consequences to making these changes. Occasionally, by asking this question we can discover if there are any small or significant reasons why we haven't made the changes we so clearly desire. Once you have identified any reasons for not being comfortable with the changes you desire then you can begin to address them.

Statement five: I have the power to influence and change these issues.

1__________2__________3__________4__________5
Disagree Agree

If you don't feel that you have the power to change these issues then, as it highlights that you expect someone else to sort out your issues for you, the Lightning Process isn't really going to be that useful for you at this point. This is because, as you have probably noticed throughout the book, influence is such a core element of the philosophy behind the success of the Process.

Statement six: I deserve to and am valuable enough to resolve my issues.

1__________2__________3__________4__________5
Disagree Agree

For those who don't have an issue with deserving and feeling valuable enough, this probably seems like a ridiculous question to answer. However, a large proportion of people do have a serious lack of self-belief. Fortunately, the Lightning Process is very useful in helping people to resolve these key stumbling blocks.

Statement seven: In terms of my issues and my ability to follow instructions, I am similar enough to all the others who have used the Process to get the results they wanted and I am bound to make the same kind of changes as them.

1__________2__________3__________4__________5
Disagree Agree

If you don't feel that you can acheive the sort of results that so many other people have using the Lightning Process then, unfortunately, you probably won't be able to until you resolve this part of your belief. This is covered extensively on the sections on placebo and expectations of success. If you scored low on this belief, please re-read that section.

I would recommend that you now go through the same seven statements but this time using the belief “Resolving my issues will be easy, rapid and permanent”.

Before contacting your Lightning Process Practitioner, spend some time considering these key seven questions and your answers. If you get low scores, ask yourself “What can I do to change this?” Both this book and the Lightning Process website are designed to help you start to shift some of these unhelpful beliefs.

What if they ask me to some homework before giving me a date for the course?

Firstly, I suggest that you see this as a good thing. It means your practitioner is being honest with you, wanting to ensure that you only take the training when they feel you have an excellent chance of getting the results you want. The LP course itself will also contain similar elements of homework, so it could also give you a taste of what attending the course will be like and help you to decide if this is the kind of course you would want to take on. I’d generally recommend doing the work and working with the practitioner to get as prepared as possible for the LP.

Chapter 16
Troubleshooting the Book

Introduction

Whilst reading this book, some of you may find that a few of the ideas, concepts and issues presented in it are a bit hard to swallow, they may cause you some concern or maybe they just don't fit with how you currently view the world. This means you probably need to do some more preparation to get the most from the course. This section is designed to assist you to get into the right place to get the best value from the Lightning Process.

Sticky Strategies

If, when working through the exercises in this book, you come up with any of the following answers or solutions then it's time to notice that you have some key strategies that are not helping you to move forwards. By that, I mean you have some ways of thinking that will almost guarantee you don't get what you want in your life and end up being stuck no matter what you try. Some common examples are:

1. "I don't know" and "I'm not sure" type answers.
2. You develop a sense of feeling totally overwhelmed by the unfamiliarity or hugeness and complexity of what you are trying to achieve.
3. You find yourself using solutions or ways of trying to sort things out which you've already used before, even though they didn't work in the past.

How to deal with the above issues:

1. "I don't know" answers have a whole section devoted to them later in this chapter.
2. Number two is resolved simply by breaking the issue down into smaller parts which will make the first step seem a reasonable possibility.
3. Number three simply tells you it's time to exercise your brain and get familiar with creating solutions, which is an

essential part of making sure you start having a life you love.

The following questions are very powerful for starting your creative processes no matter how long they have been dormant.

- If I absolutely knew I couldn't fail, that I would genuinely and totally succeed at whatever I did, what would I do?
- If I was free from all the constraints that prevent me from doing things, what would I do?
- If I could make mistakes and not get it right all of the time and if that was ok to do, what would I imagine doing?
- If I could think up things, knowing that just because I dreamed them up it didn't mean I had to actually do them, what would I dream about?
- If what I am going to do today was what I would like to leave behind as the sum of my life's path, my epitaph, the summit of all my achievement, what would I do today?

I don't know

Strange as it may seem, this is probably one of the most poisonous phrases you can ever say in your life. It has a number of different ways of appearing and you need to become wise to them all. It can appear:

- As "I don't know"
- As a blank - when you go blank
- As a pause - a pause of more than three or four seconds
- As "I'm not sure"
- As "I need to think about it"

These things are all indicative of the "I don't know" state.

The "I don't know" state is a horrific place to find yourself in because it always has very dire consequences. There is only one time when "I don't know" is okay and that is when you are asked for a factual bit of information. For example if I asked you "What is the capital of Outer Mongolia?" you may well reply “I don’t know”. But if I said to you that it is really important that I find out, then you would probably say “Well I could probably look it up and find it out for you”.

But we don’t use always “I don’t knows” in that way. Instead we sometimes use it, often unthinkingly:

- As a blocking tactic
- As a way of either avoiding getting things wrong or looking foolish
- When we just can’t be bothered to find the answer
- When we don’t want to take responsibility

In polite society we can get away with “I don’t knows”. If someone asks you a question and you respond with “I don’t know”, they will rarely question you any further, but there are huge problems as a result of using “I don’t know”.

Travel Agency Trouble

I’d like you to imagine for a moment that you are a travel agent and your job is to book a holiday for me. Imagine I answer every question that you ask with “I don’t know”.

So you would ask “Where would you like to go on holiday?” and I would reply “I don’t know”.

And you would say “Do you want to go somewhere hot or somewhere cold?” and I would reply, “I don’t really know”. So you might say, “Do you want to go somewhere relaxing or somewhere adventurous on your holiday?” and I would reply “I don’t really know”. And you’d say “Would you like to go soon or later on in the year?” and I would reply, “I don’t really know”.

What kind of holiday would you end up booking for me? Well, if you didn’t throw me out of your office for being a complete pain, you’d book me a holiday that you think I might like. But because you have no information to go on you are guessing what my preferences would be. What is the chance of me liking that holiday? Probably quite slim because you chose it and not me.

Also, as the travel agent you have to work really hard, making all the suggestions, doing all the work. “I don’t know” means that as the holiday booker, I have taken no part in the decision making process therefore if it’s not as I wanted then I can blame that ‘darned travel agent’ for choosing the wrong holiday.

When people say, “I don’t know”, they naturally avoid exerting any influence on a situation or decision. This may seem like a good deal because then they’ll never get it wrong. They’ll never be seen as making the wrong choices but it means that somebody else will design their life for them. Unfortunately, although people may help you design your life with the best will in the world, they will never design it as well as you could because they don’t know you as well as you do. I insist, when people come to see me, that they never ever use the phrase “I don’t know”. The reason for this is if you use “I don’t know” in my clinic it will make any training or therapy much longer than it needs to be and it’ll take you that much longer to get your issues sorted. So if you want to move forward in your life as quickly as possible, then I suggest you start by dumping the “I don’t know” phrase. This kind of usage of it serves absolutely no purpose whatsoever, unless you want everything to stay exactly the same.

Shifting Stuckness

I mentioned that there were two approaches for “I don’t knows”. The first, which is often very effective, is to decide to be creative whenever “I don’t know” appears and find an immediate solution. Occasionally, when you’re really stuck, you will need to ask yourself the following question, “When was the last time I found myself in a similar situation (by similar we mean another time in your life when you were stuck in some shape or form) and got myself unstuck?”

It’s true to say that there are times in everybody’s life when they become stuck. Maybe we get to the checkout at the supermarket and we find we haven’t got any money as we’ve left our wallet or purse at home. Or maybe we get to the train station and the last train has left or been cancelled and we can't get home. Or we have a flat tyre on our car and we have already used up the spare and we're stuck. We've all been in situations similar to these where we are really stuck, but interestingly enough we know you didn't stay stuck there because you're not there any more - you got through it.

So take a few moments to think about a time when you thought you were really stuck but you worked your way through it. I don't know what that time is that you're recalling, it may be a time recently, a time in the distant past, something you think about a lot or something you seldom think about. It may be in a work context, a family context or in some other context altogether but as you think about it notice what you notice about yourself and how you dealt with it. Write down how you got through the situation.

You will notice there are a number of key factors. First of all, you believed there was a way through, that's the first thing. When you got stuck at that station, for instance, and you couldn't get home, you knew you would get home eventually, but you didn't know quite when. When you had a flat tyre and you already had a flat in the spare you knew you would survive that experience, you knew you would get home eventually, it was just a question of how.

Secondly, when you get yourself into these kinds of 'stuck situations' and you've tried everything that you think will work but it doesn't (for example, you've looked at the flat tyre and you've got the spare out and that has a puncture too), you've used up all your natural options. What do you do next? You have to start thinking creatively, and that's what you did in these situations. You thought through things in a different way, believing that there was a solution and you found it.

It may be that the first solution you came up with didn't work but you knew there was an answer and you flexibly and creatively came up with it. Remember this memory, because it is vitally important. My experience tells me that 99% of people reading this book will come across "I don't know" somewhere in their lives and it will really seem to bog everything down.

If you let it get to you and think there is no solution, then it will make everything grind to a halt. If you start to approach this stuckness more creatively, in the ways I've outlined above, then you will beat that "I don't know" and start to move your life on. "I don't knows" are one of the key ways that people keep themselves permanently stuck in their lives so please make sure you are really aware of them.

Chapter 17
Phil Parker Peak Performance (P4) Training

Introduction

Many of the stories in this book recount the inspirational tales of how individuals used the LP to overcome massive difficulties against all odds. This has naturally led to people who don't have any 'issues' or health problems wanting to know if the LP could enhance their performance in other fields. The standard LP seminar is particularly focused on health and well-being and although it can also enhance your personal performance I have designed a specifically tailored programme for use in business called Phil Parker Peak Performance or P4 for short. Although it is not the same as the LP, it earns a brief place in this book, as it was designed by adapting powerful elements of the LP to suit business environments. What follows are some intriguing stories and thoughts from this new and exciting field.

Stockbroking

Gavin was one of our earliest business clients. Working with him and others helped me develop P4. He wanted to make his successful stock market trading business even more successful. Before I saw him his business was doing very well but he did notice that on days when, through no fault of his own, the markets had gone against him he had started to get into bad trading habits. This had resulted in reckless trading, where he ditched his usual, sound method for effective trading for more of a gambling mentality, trying to recapture his losses with more risky trades. This strategy, more often than not, meant he made further losses, which he again tried to reverse by more and more risky trades.

As soon as he learnt and applied the training, these bad trading losses became a thing of the past. As a result of being able to manage his state of mind to stay calm and focused when he really needed it, he was able to avoid certain kinds of behaviour that compelled him to take unnecessary risks and hence reduce his losses. His business success improved dramatically and now he's one of the most respected traders in his field.

Business Issues EXERCISE:
If you're reading this book from the perspective of a peak performer, chief executive or business manager then ask yourself what are the core issues that cause the most problems in business?

1.
2.
3.
4.
5.

My experience is that many of the issues that arise in business are ones of either poor communication between departments, customers and clients or even more importantly through poor levels of self-management.

Business Success
Looking at the core actions of a successful business, in order to get a job done effectively there needs to be:

1. An appropriate knowledge base
2. The opportunity
3. And most importantly, the ability to be in the correct state of mind to do the job

We can verify that by asking the question "If you think of a problem in your business at the moment how much simpler would it be if there was excellent communication between all parties involved?"

Also ask, "And what if the people that are part of your organisation were excellent at managing their 'own stuff' rather than avoiding dealing with the issues and problems, passing the buck or blaming other people?"

Knowledge Base

Most businesses already have, can buy in or develop knowledge bases and skills - but that doesn't necessarily make them successful.

Opportunities

All businesses have to create opportunities to be successful. This could mean anything from going to a meeting to pitch or cold calling through telesales.

Correct State of Mind

Emotional intelligence and the ideas of the value of your workforce (intellectual capital) have been highlighted a great deal recently as the keys to success, but no matter how good your workforce is, the most important question has to be, "Can they get into the right state of mind to do the job effectively, at precisely the time that they need to, all of the time?"

This is exactly what P4 delivers as it trains people to be able to make conscious decisions as to what state of mind they are in. On a very simple level this could mean knowing how to get into a state of confidence before a presentation, how to get into a creative frame of mind when needed and equally how to be able to switch off from work and get into a relaxed/non-work state of mind at the end of the day. Everyone recognises that this would be an ideal way to operate and, in fact, people who are very successful in all areas of life are able to do this already but most people just don't know how to.

Mining your Brilliance

In spite of their success, many successful business people, in a similar way to the peak athletes mentioned at the beginning of the book, aren't consciously aware of what they do to consistently generate their success. If they were then they would be excellent teachers of their success strategy and their teams would be as successful as they are. Some, but not many, successful business people are able to do this.

P4 teaches such peak performers to discover exactly how they have maintained their success, so they can either personally disseminate it throughout their organisation, or employ someone else, skilled in P4, to do it for them.

Successful business people have huge levels of effectiveness, competence and success in key areas of their lives but seem to fail to reproduce that consistency of performance in other equally key areas such as making time for themselves or family, switching off from work, losing weight, eating and drinking more reasonably etc. P4 can use your success strategies from one area and teach you how to apply your strategy for success (i.e. where you are already an expert) to an area where you'd like to be more successful.

We often say "before P4 there was just training..." and this is because there is another very valuable and unique aspect of the P4 that sets it apart from the other tools available for business success. As it's a training, once you have mastered how to apply it in one situation, you can translate those skills to any other area of your life or business, with a minimal amount of support from your trainer. In fact, most people that we train find they rarely need to contact us for support as they've realized the solutions for virtually all their issues are now available to them by just applying the tools of P4.

If you'd like to find out more about this unique approach to business performance please contact the Head Office at p4@philparker.org or visit the website **www.p4training.com**

Chapter 18
Checklist

Introduction

Now you've almost reached the end of your journey through this book, it's important to notice how far you've travelled. The following exercise is designed to ensure that you've got value from this book and have taken on the elements that will allow you to recognise if the Lightning Process is something for you at this point in time. Consider the words of Winston Churchill:

> *This is not the end, neither is it the beginning of the end, but it is the end of the beginning.*

EXERCISE:

As you read the book did you relate other people's stories to your own situation, even if they didn't have the same issues as you? Did you ask yourself "If the Process can change those issues for them, that easily, then what about mine?"

Page

8 Do you understand the dangers of prediction?

14 Do you consider the Lightning Process to be a training or a treatment?

17 Do you agree with the core concepts?

27 Do you understand what determines the Lightning Process success rates?

29 Do you understand what we mean by 'Influence'?

32 Do you understand what's required to ensure long-term success using the Process?

57 Have you discovered that the route out of CFS/ME can be easy?

77 Have you discovered that the route out of depression can be easy?

81 Have you discovered that the route out of low confidence, self-esteem and anxiety can be easy?

89 Have you discovered that the route out of weight and food issues can be easy?

93 Have you discovered that the route out of OCD can be easy?

97 Have you discovered that the route out of the symptoms of MS can be easy?

131 Have you discovered that there are programmes related to the LP for business and other environments?

I would like to leave you with one last thought, which comes from Marabel Morgan, and is key to success in any field:

> *Persistence is the twin sister of excellence. One is a matter of quality; the other, a matter of time.*

Other Publications and Courses by Phil Parker

We've included some information about some of Phil's other books, CDs and courses. The books and CDs are available from the online shop at **http://store.philparker.org** and information about Phil's courses is available on his website **www.philparker.org**

The Ten Questions To Ask For Success

Phil's first book covers the core aspects of how to get success by using the most powerful questions in the world. This book has already inspired some of the world's leaders, and has been read all around the world from the Amazon jungle, to Guam and Australia.

Dûing - The New Language of Change

This intriguing and life-changing book explores Phil's invention of a new word that was to change the lives of thousands. This new language is a cornerstone of his Lightning Process and Peak Performance programmes. Discover in detail how and when to use these new ideas to start to get powerful change in your life.

CD Audio Programmes

Phil has produced a wide range of CD titles to help you with every aspect of your life:

- Boost Your Immune System
- Deep Sleep
- Inspired Interviews
- New Year New You
- Pain Reduction and Pre-Op
- Positive Pregnancy
- Relaxation and De-Stress
- Slim Whilst You Sleep
- Stop Smoking
- Stress Free Christmas
- Unlimited Confidence

Using these, tap into Phil's knowledge and unique perspective as he guides you through using some of the best tools for change available.

Courses

Phil is constantly working to create new courses with easy access to all for the latest life changing ideas. Below are a selection of the courses which are available:

- The Lightning Process (LP)
- Building Your Future (for LP graduates)
- Phil Parker Peak Performance (P4) - for business professionals and leaders in all fields
- NLP for Business - short and longer certified courses
- Getting Creativity
- Resolving Conflict - with others and within ourselves
- Key Life Skills - all the important stuff we weren't taught in school - like how to be happy, successful and deal with life
- Getting Thin and Staying Thin - a new balanced approach to weight loss
- Language as Medicine - a seminar for health care professionals to learn how to use words to assist the healing process

For the full and latest information please go to the website: **www.philparker.org**.